mixed

messages

In loving memory of Mary Knowles.

- Paul Knowles

In memory of Marie and Vera Hanson.

- John Hanson

Marie and I support this wonderful project because everyone has lost loved ones to the dreaded disease that is cancer – if not a death sentence, it certainly is a life altering event that makes us all confront our mortality. We congratulate Paul for compiling such a marvellous tribute to cancer victims and survivors.

- Greg Voisin

We, at Challenger Motor Freight, are pleased to support this book in honor of our fellow colleagues, family members and friends who are now suffering, or have suffered, the effects of cancer and in the hope for compassionate care, effective treatment and ultimately, a cure.

- Challenger Motor Freight Charity Committee

mixed messages

• Rona Altrows • Amanda Boyden • Joseph Boyden
• Wayson Choy • Lorna Crozier • Will Ferguson
• Liz Fleming • David Francey • Lennie Gallant
• Max Gordon • Katherine Govier • Anita Hanson
• David Hobson • S.K. Johannesen • Stephen Kimber
• Barbara Kingstone • Paul Knowles • Patrick Lane
• Stuart McLean • Andrew Pyper • Paul Quarrington
• Erika Ritter • Robin Robinson • Anne Stockwell
• Jane Urquhart

ISBN 978-0-9687138-6-0

Published with the generous assistance of:
John Hanson
Greg and Marie Voisin
The Challenger Motor Frieght Charity Committee

Cover by Dave Sapelak Design Studio,
New Hamburg, Ontario, Canada

Printed by Friesens, Book Division, Altona, Manitoba

Published by English Garden Publishers
170 Shade Street
New Hamburg, Ontario, Canada
N3A 4J2
(519) 662-6757
e-mail books@englishgardenpublishers.com
www.englishgardenpublishers.com

Printed in Canada

contents

Foreword

What do you get when you ask more than two dozen of the finest writers in North America to contribute, free of charge, to a book created to raise money for cancer-related causes? You get a response rooted in generosity, compassion, creativity, relationship. You get unique and wonderful short stories, poems, creative non-fiction, lyrics. You get a book well worthy of publication, even if it were not for an important cause.

But it is, of course, for just such a cause. The 25 writers whose work is included in this book have together built a fundraising foundation that will make a difference in a number of important charitable programs, including the Hospice of Waterloo Region, brain tumour research, and many other cancer-related causes. The writers have not done this alone; three donors – Greg and Marie Voisin, the team at Challenger Motor Freight, and my great friend John Hanson – have contributed all funds necessary to publish and distribute this book. That means all income from book sales will go to cancer-related charities.

This book is a triumph on several levels. It will be a significant fundraising tool. It will raise consciousness about the important causes of cancer treatment and the search for cures to cancer.

But as a writer and editor, I am also delighted that it raises consciousness about great literature; because there is excellent writing between the covers of this volume.

I celebrate the diversity represented on our list of contributors; we have brilliant fiction writers, noted writers of creative non-fiction, excellent poets, very funny humour writers, two fine lyricists. The writers are a unique microcosm of North American culture – Canadian and American, female and male, gay and straight, of many races. What they all have in common is a love for, and great talent with, the written word.

That is perhaps the only theme identifiable across the works presented here. These writers have thought about many of the issues closest to the hearts of humankind – love, death, laughter, sex, prejudice, relationships, drag shows and whether Kraft dinner is better with or without gourmet wieners. You will, as the cliché goes, laugh, you will cry... and I know this because I have done both, every time I have re-read the manuscript. I am grateful for the incredible quality of these pieces, and as a writer, I am honoured to appear in such amazing company.

Thanks to every contributor to this book, authors, donors, and advisors... especially Nancy, who has been involved in every detail of "Mixed Messages".

-Paul Knowles

Andrew Pyper

The Quotidian Award

(An excerpt from a work-in-progress tentatively titled The Killing Circle. The novel is scheduled for publication in 2008 by Doubleday Canada.)

The Quotidian Award, better known as the Dickie, is the nation's second-richest literary prize. The honour was established in memory of Richard "Dickie" Barnham, a Presbyterian minister who, in his retirement, became an enthusiastic memoirist, recounting his salty, hardscrabble Cape Breton youth and later, the mild eccentricities of his quaint Ontario parsonage. He was also, in the year before his death, the purchaser of a $12-million winning lottery ticket. According to the wishes of his will, the Dickie is today awarded to the work of fiction that "best reflects the domestic heritage of Canadian family life," which has led to a series of hushed, defiantly uneventful winners, a rainy day parade of stolid farmers and fishermen widows.

It also happens to be the gala event of the season. A ticket to the Dickie marks one's membership to Toronto's elite, bookish or otherwise, a Who's Who of country club philanthropists, TV talking heads, publishing CEOs, and the nominees themselves, who generally recognize each other from previous shortlists. The National Star's publisher has never missed it. It's in part why, each year, a photo of the winner and a hyperventilating description of the menu and ladies' gowns appear on the front page.

It's the sort of assignment I'm no longer considered for. Even when I was the literary columnist, the paper preferred to send one of the party girls from the Style section who could recognize not only the celebrities in attendance, but the designers who did their outfits. This year, however, the reporter they had in mind called in four hours before the event to say she was at home projectile vomiting (something about bad oysters at the Givenchy fragrance launch the night before) and wouldn't be able to do the Dickies. In order to get the piece into the front section for the next morning, an eleven o'clock deadline had to be met. The Managing Editor was out of town at one of her executive retreats, so the task of choosing a last minute alternative came down to the News editor who, remembering my name from my previous life in Books, asked if I could do it for him.

I accepted. Two mistakes in a row.

The press pass allows me to take a guest. I ask Tamara, but she would rather get an early night, and Tim Earheart has another date with the temp in Human Resources. The wise course would be to go alone, write the kind of story they're looking for, and be in bed by midnight. But the idea of the Dickies and being among so many who have so much of what I'll never have brings out the critic in me, and instead of being a good boy, I call Len and ask if he'd like to come.

"You could slip someone your manuscript," I tell him.

9

"You think?"

"Every editor in town is going to be there. It's an opportunity."

"Maybe just a couple short stories," Len decides after a moment's consideration. "Something that could fit under my jacket."

By the time I rent a tux, skim the first chapters of the shortlisted books and spin by in a cab to pick up Len (who has also been fitted in black tie, though for someone a foot shorter and thirty pounds lighter than he) we arrive at the Royal York just in time to catch the last half of the cocktail hour.

"If this place blew up you'd wipe out an entire generation of writers," Len whispers on our way into the Imperial Room.

"Are you making an observation or a suggestion?"

"Look! There's Grant Duguay!"

I follow Len's pointing finger and find the emcee of tonight's proceedings. The same waxy, catalogue model with a used car salesman grin who acts as host of Canadian MegaStar!

"That's him alright. Can you hold onto this?"

I stick my empty wine glass into Len's pudgy grip and make a couple notes into my dictaphone. This motion has the effect of marking me as a journalist, which turns a few wary heads. It also draws attention to my hulking companion, who is now helpfully pointing out each elderly nominated author between excited cries of Oh! Oh! For such a packed room, people give Len and me a lot of space to ourselves.

Although he's a horror fanboy at heart, Len keeps astonishingly up to date on all the hottest publishing gossip. He knows the well-travelled stories of affairs, burned bridges, writerly feuds. But also a good deal of material I've never heard before. Now, for instance, he's waving his finger at a vaguely familiar woman across the room like it's Margaret Atwood herself. Which it can't be, as Atwood is behind us, signing her autograph for the coat check girl.

"And there! That's Rosalind Canon!"

"Who?"

Len looks at me to make sure I'm being serious. "At the Brain Pudding launch. The one who got three-quarters of a million for her first novel."

"Are you her accountant or something?"

"It's all over the blogosphere."

"You know, you're the first person I've ever heard actually say that word out loud."

I get Len to point Rosalind out to me. And there she is, the mousy girl with the six-figure publishing deal, shaking hands with every culturecrat and society wife and frocked editor in sight as though making a run for office. Even from across the room I can lip read the same earnest Thank you in reply to the congratulations, over and over. It makes me want to say the same thing to someone. A passing waiter will have to do.

"Thank you," I say, plucking a pair of martinis from his tray.

I'm halfway through the second when the Prime Minister rings the bell for dinner. This gets a few astonished laughs from Len, who can't believe he's so close to all these people he normally sees only on television. "It's funny," he says as we make our way toward the table reserved for the press at the back of the room. "Just being around celebrities makes you feel like you're the one who's famous."

11

"Watch it. It's lines like that that'll get you a column somewhere."

We settle in a few seconds before the other hacks arrive so that I'm able to stick one of the two bottles of wine on the table between my feet, just in case the steward is unavailable at a crisis point later on. Then the plastic MegaStar! guy is up at the lectern saying something about how reading made him what he is today, which seems reasonably true, given that managing a teleprompter would be tricky for an illiterate.

Following this, as the dinner begins to be served, each of the nominated authors take the stage to talk about the genesis of their work. The bottle between my feet is empty before you can say gag reflex.

It's absurd and I know it. It's shallow and unfounded and generally reflects poorly on my character. Because I haven't published a book. Haven't written a book. I don't have anything in mind to one day turn into a book. But in the spirit of full and honest disclosure, this is what I'm thinking as I sit in the Imperial Room in my itchy tux watching the night's honourees bow into the waves of applause: Why not me?

After dessert, Mr. MegaStar! introduces Mrs. Dickie Barnham to announce the winner of this year's Quotidian Award. It takes five calls for quiet before anyone can hear the name widow Barnham croaks into the microphone. And once I've jotted it down on the back of my hand, I'm out of there. "I'm off, Len. Got to write this thing up lickety-split."

Len eyes my untouched maple syrup cheesecake. "Are you going to eat that?"

"All yours."

I squeeze his shoulder as I get up from the table, and

although Len smiles in acknowledgment of the friendly gesture, the fact is if I hadn't grabbed him I would have fallen face first into a passing tray of beaver shaped shortbreads.

* * *

"I'm curious," the Managing Editor says, her face approximating an expression of real curiosity. "What were you thinking when you wrote this?"

It's the next morning. All three of us — me, my sour stomach and imploding head — have been called in to the Managing Editor's office. She has the front page of today's National Star laid out over her desk. My by-line under the lead story. "Prodigious Pay-Off for Pedantic Prizewinner."

"You mean the headline?" I say. "I've always been a sucker for alliteration."

"I'm speaking of the piece itself."

"I don't know. I thought it needed some colour, I suppose."

The Managing Editor looks down at the paper. Reads aloud some of the lines she has highlighted. "'Proceedings interrupted by coughing fits from an audience choking on air thick with hypocrisy.' ... 'The real prize should have gone to the jury for managing to read the shortlist.' ... 'The Literary Discovery of the Month, Rosalind Canon, 24, was also in attendance, smiling as only a typing monkey who happens to bang out 200 coherent pages and be rewarded with an advance that can buy a million bananas can smile.' ... 'There was more irony in listening to the host of an execrable TV show preach the virtues of reading than in the past dozen Dickie winners.' And so on."

The Managing Editor lifts her eyes from the page. I

have to hand it to her. The only tell I can detect of her homicidal thoughts is a single twitch of her left brow.

"Colour, Patrick?"

I search for a way to apologize. Because I am sorry. And I have at least a handful of plausible excuses to back up my regret. A sleepless wife, the painful symptoms of writer's block, pop culture overexposure. A ghoul circling my house. But as I clear my throat to try them out, the Managing Editor reaches for the phone.

"Who are you calling?"

"Security."

"That won't be necessary."

"I know. I just rather like the idea of having you escorted out."

"This is it, then?"

"Very much so."

"Would it make any difference if I said I was sorry?"

"None whatsoever." She raises a finger to silence me. "Ah yes, could you please have Patrick Rush removed from the building? He's in my office. That's right, this is a permanent access denial situation. Thanks."

The Managing Editor hangs up. Gives me a smile that's actually something else. The bared teeth dogs use to show their willingness to rip another's lungs out.

There's no accounting for it. There really isn't. But even though this is by far the worst day of my less-than-spectacular journalistic career, I can't help being fond of this woman.

"So, Patrick," she says, her lips pulling back to show a pair of pointy incisors. "How's the family?"

Paul Quarrington

The Conversion

I was worried over whether or not to have a piece of pie – the waitress stood in front of a display case, her arms swept up towards the baked goods as if she was the lovely Carol, as in, Carol, please show our contestants what they could win today – when my wife returned from the washroom. It did not seem to me she had been gone a particularly long time. Or, to be more truthful and exact – which you, Mr. Becker, told me is one of the purposes of Creative Writing, the hunting down of truth and exactness – she had been gone a long time, but not much longer than usual. My wife Ruth always spent a long time because her "internal plumbing," which I'd long found baffling, had become even more so as she passed the sixty-year mark. So, I was not in anyway suspicious or dismayed or angered. I believe that's truthful and exact. I was, as I've stated, worried over whether or not to have a piece of pie, food that has been denied me for a long, long while.

We were on holiday – a driving tour of Ontario's summery northlands, a leisurely, even lethargic expedition, our first holiday since what Ruth called the "fateful day," which made it sound like it was something that happened in a story rather than to her, to us – and I thought a piece of pie might somehow be in the cards, as if this piece of pie, so far from home, would not add an ounce to my three hundred and eight pounds. I further believed it might be in the cards because Ruth had ordered a beer with her lunch, which she drank straight from the bottle. This was not overwhelmingly odd, I'd seen Ruth drink beer before, especially on hot sweltering days such as dwelt outside the diner, but it did throw a little wrinkle into the northern day and make me believe – the waitress pointed to the Cherry and licked her lips – that a piece of pie might be in the cards.

So when Ruth sat down I said, "The Cherry pie," not knowing what point I was going to make, I only thought to draw attention and focus to the display case of baked goods. At any rate, I searched Ruth's eyes then – expecting, I'll admit, a flash of dull fire, it being her apparent mission in life to make sure I adhere to my various diets – and saw that they were strange. I expect you to circle that word, Mr. Becker, imbued as it is with inexactness, but I believe I'll stick to my guns here. Strange, those eyes were, looking more like knots in a tree than anything that belongs in a human face. And she said, "I've accepted Jesus as my Lord and personal Savior."

I did what I think most human beings would do under the circumstances, I asked my wife to repeat herself. Ruth was happy to do this, as the very speaking of the words seemed to be a thrill, turning her cheeks red and widening her gray eyes. "I have opened my heart and accepted Jesus as my Lord and personal Savior."

I stared at the placemat in front of me, which was

entitled "Hinterland Denizens." The wolverine was depicted in pre-fight mode, as in, hindquarters reared up, razor-sharp teeth bared. "Well," I said, "that's, er, nice," but there were a few points to clear up, such as this: "You say this happened whilst you were in the washroom?"

My wife produced from her lap a tiny book, more a miniature magazine. She gave it to me in a manner that took twice as long as giving should, as if she were hesitant to lay the thing upon my clammy palm. Ruth said, "This was on the washroom floor. Isn't that wonderful?"

As I accepted it I remarked inwardly that all this was due to a basic truth of human nature, that a person can't sit upon the "throne" without reading material. We have all – you, I and the Queen – sat in those tiny rooms and studied the chemical make-up of Borax Cleanser. How sneaky – sneaky as in its strongest sense, sneak attack Pearl Harbour type of thing – of these Christians, to bait that particular trap. For, to be truthful and exact, my declarations of niceness notwithstanding, something inward warned me life as I knew it was essentially over, my few pleasures torn away. For instance, on Monday nights I visit the Apollo, a small tavern in my hometown of Hamilton, Ontario. The Apollo is decorated with depictions of space travel, and a paper maché full-size model of a lunar module, or whatever they're called, is suspended from the ceiling. I sit at a large table with "friends" of mine, friends such as my father had friends. Professional men. They include a high school teacher, an actuary, a fellow who repairs broken time-pieces. Truth to tell, I'm not sure exactly what several of them do. These are not friends as in oh, hi, Charlie, come in and join us for dinner, these are friends as my father had friends, as in your political thinking is faulty, your knowledge of profession-

17

al football is faulty at best, I disbelieve that particular tale of sexual derring-do. At any rate, I sit and drink (diet pop and light beer for me) with these men, we watch the football game on giant screens. This has been going on for years, this Monday night ritual, and somewhat to my shame I will admit that I allowed Ruth to labour under the misconception that the National Football League season extends the year round.

But at that moment I could feel my trips to the Apollo Room fading away, and in a "worst-case scenario" being replaced by some sombre trek to a prayer meeting.

The little book was entitled "Is This Your Life?" It was a comic book, really, each page a single black-and-white panel. I took a brief flip through, enough to note that the artist attended no school in France. (I believe it is France that contains wonderful art schools, if not, I'm certain you'll pick me up on it, Mr. Becker; also, if not France, where exactly?) He/she was also clearly more interested in drawing the Devil than Jesus, for the former was an intricate assemblage of horns, tail, pitchfork and matted fur, while the latter was a bland fellow walking around in a housecoat.

All this was not a complete surprise. Ruth had been moving on the edge of something like it for a long while. In the television room she would sit in the Ortho-Master with the remote aimed at the entertainment centre, and with the remote she would circle the frequencies, and I soon saw that she was as a hawk and the televangelists as field mice, she would draw closer and closer and spend longer and longer on their stations. She would snort disdainfully when the laying on of hands commenced, she would quickly veer off to a soap opera or Wheel of Fortune. I surmised that it was not the healing itself that angered her, rather the quality of the afflictions. Ruth had no patience for, as an instance, people who "pee and moan" about chronic back pain. She seemed to feel chronic back pain was part and parcel of the human condition, and while you may well acquire an Ortho-Master (0% financing, two years of easy payments) you may not grovel in front of faithhealers. But at the back of all this, of course, for Ruth, was the huge pain, the huge hole, that was the thing that wanted attention and needed the Lord's touch.

We are not, or have not been up until now, religious people. My wife maintained a certain piety, left over from her childhood, as in, she said grace before most meals and wouldn't do anything even vaguely fun on the Sabbath. Instead, she gave her Sundays over to jigsaw puzzles. She began with smallish reproductions of the masters, but of late had been doing abstractions with many thousand tiny pieces.

She also says her nightly prayers, does my wife. Ruth doesn't kneel beside the bed, she does it whilst she brushes her teeth. The words come out quietly, obscured by foam. Ruth asks for things like universal understanding and world peace, then she slips in a meek entreaty for a general, all-purpose forgiveness. She spits, rinses, climbs into our bed.

What I'm saying is, she had been tapping at the Almighty's door now for some time, ever since that "fateful day," and now this crude little comic book found on the floor of the diner's washroom had emboldened her so that she barged right on in there.

I stirred myself around in my seat, shifting my huge hams. The waitress brought over the bill, her arithmetical work done in a very small, precise hand. I drew read-

19

ing glasses out of my shirt pocket, balanced them on my nose and stared for a long moment at the figures. Ordinarily Ruth would have pulled the bill out of my hand, she would quickly check the total and then ruthlessly calculate the tip, it being her opinion that I am much too generous, weakened by youth and beauty, moved to pity by age or general ineptitude. But Ruth made no move now, she cradled her hands on her lap and stared at me. Ruth's eyes had acquired a new kind of softness, as in, she had so little interest in the real world, this vale of tears, that she couldn't even be bothered focussing on it. So I pulled bills out of my shirt pocket, and I did in fact leave a full four dollars as a gratuity, mostly because this waitress had wanted me to eat pie.

Actually though – truth and exactness, correct, Mr. Becker? – the reason I am soft on waitresses in general is that I have a feeling that if we'd ever had children (Ruth's baffling "internal plumbing" forbade that) we would have had, I think, two girls, and as teenagers they would have worked part-time at a diner similar to this one. They would have had their names stitched on to their uniforms, and often as I imagine them they become so clear in my mind that I am almost able to read those names.

When this waitress came to collect her money, she brought with her the pyrex coffee pot and very deftly refilled my cup. Ruth, when offered the same, shook her head, a small gentle gesture. Oh my, I suppose I thought, now coffee's on the "s–t list." I therefore resolved to enjoy this last cup, and when my hand went to the little china bowl my fat fingers latched on to a paper pouch of real sugar. Avoiding, you see, the bitter artificial sweeteners. I shook it so quickly that it was but a blur (Ruth didn't seem much interested at any rate) and I covered the tear-ing-open and dumping by musing aloud.

"Jesus, hmm? Your Lord and personal Saviour. My-my."

"I want you to."

I was stirring now and felt pleased with my successful sugar subterfuge, so pleased that I didn't see the bog I was stepping into. "You want me to what, dearest?"

"I want you to accept Jesus as your Lord and personal Saviour. I want you to open your heart."

I think that part of my brain had been thinking along these lines, that this newfound Born Again Christianity would stick around like, for example, an interest in water-colours or a desire to learn a foreign language, as in, not for long. You know what people are like. This statement is bound to get a rise out of you, Mr. Becker, you will likely make the point that if everyone already knows what people are like, why bother bashing away at the old Creative Writing? My counter-point is, I really have no insight into others, and I think that Creative Writing, for me at any rate, is a way of acquiring insight into one's own self, and shortly (in terms of the story) I am to do something unexpected, something I would never have dreamt that a man like myself would do, and it is an explanation for this odd moment which I mean both to give and to receive.

But before this comes, you need a bit more background information, as in, what happened on that "fateful day." Fair enough. It was more accurately a night, a Monday night, which meant that I was with my "friends" at the Apollo. Monday Night Football raged upon the big screens. The Apollo boasts huge six-foot screens, but these affairs are more like stained bedsheets and the images upon them are ghostly and indistinct. It was two

21

days past Christmas, and this was the year's final Monday night match-up, so it held a special significance vis a vis the post season. I'd wagered ten dollars with the high school teacher, placing my money on the team from San Francisco. The high school teacher acted upon predictions made by his personal computer, my judgement was based upon an oft-quoted credo that we Apollo men had adopted: "Never bet against Joe Montana."

It had been a curiously warm Christmas. Ruth and I had even taken an afternoon stroll wearing only the sweaters we had given each other, hers adorned with an image of a deer startled at the waterpond, mine with a rearing moose, although I did not think, to be truthful and exact, that moose rear. And this warmness had lasted, and the calls for snow brought only light rains. It was sometime in the first quarter that the temperatures started to plummet. I didn't notice, didn't even think, because I was quaffing diet soft drinks, arguing with my friends and watching the pale transmission from San Francisco, California. There was one gal in the stands wearing only a bikini, and the cameraman lingered on her quite often, and it never did occur to me that outside the Apollo's thick iron door the world was turning into ice. Had I known, I would have started to worry, because Ruth had gone to Toronto in order to visit Mrs. Dougherty, a bitter dowager with whom my wife was somehow related. Ruth believed that the Christmas holidays were for visiting friends and family, which I don't argue, but we had done our meagre circuit, we had seen my brother and his years-younger wife, we had spent an evening with my alcoholic nephew, who got very drunk and threw us out. On Ruth's side of the family there was a cousin, Herman, who believed many strange things, and there was this

22

mystery-relative Mrs. Dougherty. I drew the line at Mrs. Dougherty, she seemed to like nothing and no one on this planet, and to drive one hour each way in order to suffer abuse at her withered hands was too much.

But my wife Ruth had driven to Toronto that night, and when the ice storm started she decided she'd head for home, which of course was a miscalculation. The thing to do would have been to ride the tempest out, if even in the company of sour old Mrs. D., and to wait for the salting trucks to hulk through the night. But Ruth climbed into our car, an American-built cruising sedan (I need such a thing to accept my bulk) which is near-useless on treacherous roads.

Ironically, Ruth survived the QEW and the 403. Many cars were crumpled against retainers and guard rails, but Ruth piloted the car without mishap all the way into the city. Now, what I never got a chance to tell you (and Mr. Becker, you'll undoubtedly say that this is the least best moment, terrifically awkward and so forth, but I hope you see this isn't a "story" per se) is that we live atop the mountain. Hamilton, Ontario is, as you know, built on a mountain, a low-grade by Tibetan standards, a mountain all the same, and the Buick was halfway up the side when it lost its grip. Ruth pumped the brakes, so she says and I believe her, this is the correct procedure, but even so the wheels locked, and the car slid uselessly backwards and hit the car behind. This other car, a small foreign compact, had even less purchase upon the globe than the sedan. It sailed over the side of the world, and the father survived, the mother and infant did not.

The collision stopped Ruth's progress, if progress is the right word, stopped it dead, as if the Buick was a huge curling stone that just made a take-out. It sat quietly on the side of the ice-covered mountain and waited for the police to come. When the squad car arrived, Ruth climbed meekly into the back. She crossed her thin wrists as if she expected them to be manacled. Ruth was surprised when the policemen drove her home.

To have not added to the number of children in the world had always nettled Ruth; to have subtracted from it destroyed her. It turned her sour. She climbed into the Ortho-Master and prowled the frequencies, and I noticed that she was as a hawk and the televangelists as field mice. Myself, I continued going to the Apollo on Monday nights, and when the football season ended I said nothing. Then I proclaimed an undying allegiance to the Toronto Maple Leafs of the National Hockey League, a deep need to watch the televised game each Wednesday. I was delighted to find all my "friends" waiting for me at the Apollo. On Tuesday nights I hid in the den and did the bookkeeping, paid the bills, fifteen minutes of effort which I stretched into the work of hours. I joined a bowling league that met on Sunday evenings, and was pleased to find that once I set my three hundred and eight pounds in forward motion it imparted a lethal juggernaut effect to the ball, and at the end of the winter season I was named Novice of the Year. In short, Mr. Becker, I found ways to avoid Ruth for all the days of the week, except for Thursday, which is, you'll note, the evening you hold your Creative Writing classes.

I am sending you this from a place called Kashamanongaway, Ontario. That's an Ojibway word meaning Holy Mountain, or so they tell us. It more likely means something along the lines of "fairly steep hill," because that's what's here. At the top of the mountain/hill is a camp, a collection of cabins, tents and Airstreams.

This is the "Kashamanongaway Christian Colony" and Ruth and I are residents and intend to remain so. I will not be attending any more Creative Writing Classes. (Although I have been working on some inspirational poetry and was hoping that if you have some time you might give it a glance-over.) Because what I did back there in the diner is, when my wife told me to open my heart, I did so. After a moment's reflection I leant back in my chair and opened my heart, which was somehow an athletic endeavour, not unlike putting the shot or hurling the caber. In moments I was weeping, my face awash with warm salty tears. I murmured the name of Christ our Lord, I gave thanks. And now I am a rabid Born Again Christian and considered a zealot even by my fellows here at the Kashamanongaway Christian Colony, and that's going some.

But between you and me, Mr. Becker, I am not so rabid a proselyte as all that. I become bored during Bible study, what has been taken by my brethren as advanced bliss is actually slumber. And although I love our Lord Jesus, I tend to think of him as just another smiling face at the Apollo's round table. Because what I did back there in the diner was, I opened my heart, not for Jesus to enter, but that so my wife could, her own heart healed and whole.

Max Gordon

The Possibilities of Pleasure

Several weeks before she died, my mother and I had a conversation.

I was standing in her kitchen cooking dinner, which I ended up burning because I was flustered. She was sitting in her wheelchair with a purple shawl around her shoulders. It was April, and there had been a chill in the house. I couldn't remember how our conversation had begun that day, but since they all ended up at the same place, it didn't matter.

"Give yourself some time to figure things out," she begged. "How do you know what you want? You're still a child in so many ways, Maxie. You shouldn't choose a label until you are absolutely sure what it means. And you definitely shouldn't run around telling the whole world about this thing."

"I'm sure I'm gay, Mom," I said.

"You can't see how much you're limiting yourself. Why don't you at least wait until you've explored all the options?"

I asked her if she would give the same advice to my

sister; if she would sit her down after several dates with men and advise her not to be too hasty about her hetero- sexuality; to have sex with a woman or two first before she made any final decisions.

She recoiled in disgust. "Stop twisting my words. It's not the same thing, Maxie, and you know it."

"Why not?"

"Because homosexuality is always an easier choice. Anyone can choose to engage in homosexual behavior, but being a heterosexual requires courage."

"Well, you obviously haven't dated in the gay commu- nity," I told her. I wanted my laugh to sound effortless, but the conversation, as usual, had worked on me, and I was losing my advantage under my mother's penetrating stare. "Fighting for your rights is hard no matter who you are. How is it easier to be a homosexual when there is so much homophobia in the world? As Black people we know what it's like to be discriminated against for who we are. I'm surprised you can't find more compassion for gay peo- ple. It's the same struggle, Mom."

"It is not the same struggle and wash that chicken more carefully before you put it in the oven, you've barely rinsed it." I took the Cornish hen out of the pan and car- ried it back over to the sink, remembering that my moth- er could always argue with me and still maintain her usual hypervigilance.

"My friend Scott talked to his mother when he came out, and she had a hard time at first too, but one day she changed her mind, and they are good friends now. He does hair professionally and his mom gets her hair done in his shop all the time."

"Is your friend Scott white?"

"Yes."

27

"I thought so. Please don't compare me to a white woman."

"What's the difference?"

"The different is I'm black. And I'm your mother."

"From the standpoint of societal oppression, gayness and blackness are very similar."

"Oh, I can't stand that!" She slammed her balled-up fists in her lap and turned her head to the window in distress. "For the last time, being black and being gay are not at all the same, and I wish you people would stop comparing the two. You were born black. There is nothing wrong with being black."

"And I was also born gay, and there is nothing wrong with that either. And I'm the one who is both, so I think I would be the expert on that, not you."

"You're not the expert on anything, including yourself. You barely even know who you are anymore. I was there when you were born and you were not gay."

"How the hell did you know? Did you ask me? God, this conversation is such bullshit!"

Her voice was quiet. "Don't shout at me, Maxie, I'm still your mother."

"Well, stop disrespecting me," I told her. "I'm your son."

"I know you're my son. I raised you."

"So what? That doesn't mean you know everything about me. There are a lot of things you don't know about me."

"You're absolutely right about that," she said. "You've definitely changed. And not for the better, I might add."

"Well, so have you." I slammed the oven door shut.

Her eyes teared up. "I never should have sent you to U of M."

"What does the University of Michigan have to do with this?"

"They were the ones who told you it was okay to be a homosexual. You never used words like homophobia before. I should have sent you to a black school. You should have gone to Morehouse."

"Because there are no black gay men at Morehouse?" I didn't need to force that laugh.

"Go ahead. You think everything's funny these days. Don't worry, I won't be around much longer for you to laugh at. But you remember what I said. This gayness isn't you. You don't even remember what you were like when you were a baby. You were so sweet and curious. Now look what's happened. Maybe someone hurt you when I wasn't around. I did my best but I couldn't protect you from everything. I know your father and I made some mistakes. We probably fought too much in front of you and your sister."

"You did, and I'm dealing with that in therapy. But my sexuality is not your mistake, Mom. For once, if you can imagine, this doesn't have anything to do with you. You don't get any credit, good or bad. This is mine."

"Well, you can certainly have it."

"I watched you two fight constantly, and that affects my relationships. The only model I have for a partnership is bitchy sarcasm or violence. I'm going to have to unlearn that."

"You and your sister. But do you think I had a better model growing up? You didn't know your father when I fell in love with him. He was a different man, then. Things changed. This whole thing is his fault, by the way."

"My being gay isn't about you or Dad, or anybody's

fault, it's about me trying to live my own life. You don't get a vote and you're not going to manipulate me with your guilt, whether you are dying or not. My therapist said the other day, 'One life per customer'. You have yours, Dad has his, and I get mine to do whatever I want. You don't get to have my life too, Mom, even if you are my mother." The words tumbled out of my mouth like lines from a stage play, I'd rehearsed them so often in my therapist's office and for years in my own head. I awaited her reaction.

"Your therapist." She gave me a dubious frown. "I guess he says it's okay for you to be gay too. Is he gay?"

I hesitated for a moment and decided on the truth. "Yes."

"How are you going to get any help, Maxie, if you keep talking to the people who support this thing?" she pleaded.

"I don't need any help, Mom, at least not that kind."

"You're sick and you don't even know it."

"I'm definitely sick, but not because I'm gay."

"Well, I'm your mother, not some therapist, and I know what's best for you."

"How could you know what's best for me more than me?"

Her eyes narrowed. "You're a Republican, aren't you?"

"No, I am not a Republican! Stop changing the subject."

"That is the subject. I don't even know who I'm talking to anymore. You sound exactly like your father."

"And you're not going to get me to change my mind by shaming me with that one, either. I know all your tricks, Mom."

She was crying freely now. "You wrote your father a

loving note saying 'Dad, I'm gay, I hope you understand.' After the way he treated you all those years. With me, you just blurted it out cruelly. You didn't even write me a lovely note on nice stationery or anything."

"I didn't blurt anything. You dragged me out of the closet, remember? You asked me if I was gay that night I came home from that party at Stacey's. What was I supposed to say? I wasn't going to tell you anything for another year or two, until I figured it out myself, but you demanded an answer. You wouldn't let me go to bed that night until I told you the truth."

"You used to tell me everything. I knew you were hiding something. You were so secretive, going out all the time. Not saying where you'd been or coming home and going straight to your room. You lied and told me you were bisexual. You tricked me, Maxie."

"I didn't feel safe talking to you. Sometimes when you drank too much you were mean, and I thought you'd start a fight with me."

"So now you're gay because I drank too much. Are you going to blame your whole life on me? I guess your therapist told you I was an alcoholic, too. I never missed a day of work and you never went without anything you wanted. I might have had too much to drink a couple of times after your father and I got divorced..."

"It's not your fault I'm gay, Mom. Look, I'm sorry I lied. But I thought you were going to stop paying my college tuition and force me to come home or throw me out of the house. I couldn't take that chance."

"I'd never throw you out of the house for that, white people do that to their kids. If you'd told me that you thought you were gay sooner, when you were in high school making a decision about this, we could have gotten

31

you some therapy when it would have made a difference. Not now that you've already made up your mind and you're running around telling anyone who will listen. There is nothing wrong with questioning your life, but you are so determined these days to be right about everything, no one can tell you anything anymore."

"You know, there is another option here. You could just accept me for who I am."

"I'll never accept this because it isn't you."

"Fine." I was exhausted. In the silence, I could hear the television blaring *Jeopardy!* in her bedroom. "Dinner will be ready soon," I said. "I'll set the table."

I had to step around her chair to leave the kitchen and she stopped me with her voice. "Wait. I want to say something else. You've forgotten everything, haven't you? Do you even remember your childhood at all?"

I replied, "Actually, Mom, I remember a lot more than you think." Our eyes locked briefly, and I gave my mother the look that only an oldest child can give a parent; of shared secrets and family horror stories from the crypt that no one ever talks about. Younger children somehow manage to forget, but the oldest child always remembers.

My mother pushed the lever on her chair and backed away from the kitchen and the rest of the conversation. I watched her glide over to the table, a pro now at using her electric wheelchair. She had resisted it so much at first, and now it was almost like another body part. She even had her favorite bumper stickers on it, "Living Life In The Fast Lane," and slogans like that. She had gone from falling occasionally on the ice when I was in high school, to taping up her legs with braces under her boots so no one would know she was getting sicker, to canes, to walkers, until finally she couldn't move her legs anymore and had to submit to a wheelchair if she wanted to leave the house at all. My sister, her caretaker, who had taken a much needed break and was visiting a friend for the weekend, had fixed her hair into two tiny braids. My mother was as indomitable as ever, and a pain in the ass, but in her nightgown and slippers, and her braided hair, she was cuter than ever. When had her body gotten so small? I had gone from five to twenty-seven and my mother, was a tiny little woman in a wheelchair. I brought her a glass of water as an olive branch and sat down beside her at the table.

"Damn, I could really use a cigarette right now," she said. "Why the hell did I ever quit smoking? As stressful as living around you kids is? Why do you always start fights with me anyway, Maxie?" She shook her head wearily and glared at me. Whatever we thought about each other now, on this final twist in the road, one thing was for sure: we'd definitely been through a lot in twenty-seven years.

"You started it, Mom, as always," I reminded her. "And you stopped smoking because it was killing you." She looked up and we were struck by the irony at the same time, relieved finally to find a laugh we could share.

When I was seven, I would go to the store to get my mother's cigarettes. The Shop-Rite was several blocks from where we lived. My friends and I asked for money to buy candy, and my mother would say, "Well if you're going, you might as well save me a trip. I'll write you a note." On the way, I took the note out of my pocket and read it. On a piece of yellow legal pad paper in her fluid script, it said: "To Whom It May Concern, I have given my son permission to buy these cigarettes for me, as I am unable to leave the house at the moment. If you need to confirm this, please call me at this number."

My mother smoked in private, or at least in as much privacy as she could find in a house with two kids. She was already a woman of considerable glamour, but watching her sitting on the edge of her bed smoking with her legs crossed, obscured by the rising spiral of smoke, with her head tilted slightly and her hair falling on her shoulders, the image was an irresistible invitation to the mystery of that particular compulsion. It wasn't just the way she held the cigarette that was compelling, it was the wall of silence that surrounded her; no matter how insistent the noises outside her door, or outrageous the demands on her, a cigarette break created an impenetrable shield, a space that was distinctly hers, "a room of one's own." In that space she was invulnerable and safe – we were encouraged not to come near her. I have to assume now, on reflection, that there were many times when she probably wanted to get away from our family, away from two children, the demands of a husband, and the responsibility of having three people who counted on her. A parent must be bewildered from time to time, waking up in the morning to find that there are two human lives that didn't exist in the world before, who now require constant supervision and care. Just one of those mornings you must get up and wonder what it was like when you only had to care about what you wanted for breakfast, what your plans were for the day, what clothes you were going to wear. Now the first thought after opening one's eyes in the morning after, "Okay, I'm still alive," was, "Where are the kids right now and what are they doing?"

Sometimes I would catch my mother smoking and crying. Occasionally she wept, but most of the time she

just sat there with tears on her face. I came in from playing to get a drink of juice and found her standing by the
window with a faraway stare, holding her cigarette, arms
folded, and looking as if she couldn't see out of the window, even though it wasn't dark outside or raining. I
asked her why she was crying.

"Because I'm sad," she said.

"Why are you sad?"

"Your mother's just sad sometimes. It's okay for me to
be sad. Now, you go back outside and play." She wiped
her eyes briefly and smiled. "Don't worry, honey, I'll be
fine."

I didn't understand then that cigarettes sometimes
helped people look at things they wished they could forget. You could consider an intolerable past, protected by
the rising curtain of smoke. I knew there were things that
had happened to my mother in her life that made her cry,
but I didn't know what they all were. She had nightmares
from time to time from which she woke up screaming.
One night she was straightening her hair at the stove
after the house had gone to sleep, and I awoke. Waiting
until she put her hot comb down, I snuck up behind her
and shouted, "Boo!" She wasn't even angry with me; she
just sat down and cried, rocking back and forth, and told
me for reasons she couldn't explain to me, to please never
surprise her like that again.

I always wanted to protect my mother, but I couldn't
save her from everything, in fact I couldn't save her from
anything at all, but sometimes I wrote her notes I
thought would help her or at least might make her happy.
My graphics became more sophisticated with age, until I
had the money to buy Hallmark cards, but the content
was always the same: "Mom, I love you and I want you to

be happy." No matter how carefully I colored them, or started over to make them perfect, no matter how many freshly sharpened crayons I used, or trails of paper I'd balled up in frustration because the card had to be just right, it never kept her from going to her private place where tears in front of dark windows waited for her. She left me behind when she went to that place, but she always took her cigarettes with her.

I thought of my mother and days when she would be getting ready for work and running late. She and my father would pick up whatever argument they hadn't finished from the night before, and she'd pause from putting on her make-up to throw a few nasty words at him over her shoulder. She was half-dressed and running around in her bra, leaving behind a cloud of talcum powder and perfume while the television blared a morning news show. I asked her where she'd last seen my other shoe. "I don't wear your shoes, Maxie. They are probably wherever you left them yesterday." My sister could find only one barrette which she held in one hand and a hairbrush in the other, imploring my mother to help her finish getting ready for school; a permission slip needed to be created for a school trip because it was the last day to turn one in and the original had been lost; a lunch money envelope required a check or otherwise there would be no hot lunch the following week. My mother held her compact in one hand and tried to study her face and apply mascara, while my father shouted something about unpaid bills, mortgages and debt. I asked her to drop me off at school on her way to work because I was late again and there wasn't time for me to walk to school. My sister moaned it wasn't fair, that she wanted a ride if I was getting one. My father blared that both of us should have to walk and be late; it would serve us right for not going to bed when he told us to last night, and when he was a kid, he never had half the privileges we had, and he was still expected to perform in school. Someone had accidentally tripped over the curling iron and unplugged it and my mother didn't have time to fix her hair, so she took a wig from her drawer and brushed it vigorously, getting an orange smudge on the collar of her blouse as she tried to put it and her lipstick and her shoes on at the same time. When I asked her if she was ready to leave yet because I was going to be late, she grabbed the brush from my sister and snatched it through her hair as my sister yelled. My father roared at my mother that it was her fault that everything was so disorganized and why the hell didn't she deal with these damn kids who never cleaned up their rooms but wanted everything including being chauffeured to school, and she stood in the middle of the room, in her coat, and couldn't find her keys which had been on the dresser, and I told her they were downstairs on the kitchen counter because I'd gone out to her car to get a tape I wanted to listen to last night, and my father reminded her about my dentist appointment that afternoon and asked if she was planning to take me because he had a meeting, and her purse slipped down off her shoulder onto the floor. My sister asked why she was crying. "I just can't cope!" she sobbed. "Do you hear me? I'm telling you, I can't cope with my life anymore!"

Women never drink, especially mothers. When fathers move out, they come home from work and stay behind bathroom doors for hours asking to be left alone, please, just for a little while. They eventually go into their bedrooms and silently close the door behind them. There are never any bottles when a mother drinks but sometimes an empty half-pint of vodka is found under the couch where you are vacuuming, behind a set of towels in the bathroom after a shower, or in the cupboard back behind the cereal. You learn to make your own dinner, to write your own permission slips, to walk quietly through the house, and leave the closed door alone.

My mother died in 1998, at 58. Her death certificate said, "Respiratory failure from spinal muscular atrophy", but I felt as if she'd been assassinated. When I returned to New York after her funeral, I went straight to a gay bar. I leaned against the wall drinking and staring at the revelers who were drunk and bored with each other, standing in the bar waiting for something different and fantastic to happen to them that hadn't happened when they'd stood in the same places twenty-four hours before. The pounding beat of the house music helped to ease the palpable despair that hung in the air. I wondered how the world had the audacity to go on when my mother was dead. Intellectually, I knew it was ridiculous to believe someone had killed her; diseases "just happened" to people, and when they did, it was always tragic, but never anyone's fault. Yet I couldn't help thinking, if my mother had been a white woman, would she have died at 58? Sure, there were white women who died much younger, but would she have died at 58 if she'd been a white man? Maybe my mother would have died at 58 whether she'd been an Amish farmer, a New York taxi driver or the prime minister of a foreign nation. But I couldn't stop thinking about black people, and black women, and daughters with abusive fathers, and stress, and diet, and poverty, and racism and sexism, and energy that should be used for jogging in the park, or salsa dancing, or a gourmet cooking class, energy for self-love, that was used up every day instead on dignity, survival, on fighting against being overwhelmed by oppression or domestic violence, on trying to cope with childhood memories of violation and narrow escapes from harm. And finally the nightmares from memories when one didn't escape and was finally, devastatingly harmed. The energy-sapping existence that a black life demanded every day. I wanted to go after her killer, but whom? How do you kill America, racism, lynching, promotions denied because of gender inequality? I couldn't determine where social violence ended and where personal responsibility began. Maybe she would have lived longer if she'd given up red meat, alcohol and cigarettes a decade sooner. It was this dynamic, the personal versus political, that always allowed America's greatest serial killer, social injustice, to go free.

None of it had seemed real the month before her death: the interview with the hospice worker, the discussion about funeral arrangements. There were to be no speeches by overblown relatives looking for an opportunity to self-aggrandize; we were to order lots of flowers, and no music. In the quiet, people would be left to their private reflections and thoughts. We might have been talking about someone else that day, a distant cousin or great aunt. My sister and I listened carefully as my mother insisted that we make her appear as beautiful in death as she'd attempted to look daily in life. (I was especially thankful for this conversation later; it gave us the courage gently to ask the woman from the funeral home who prepared my mother to reconsider some of the makeup. The rouge the woman had chosen was raspberry-colored and wrong – ghoulish and overdone, like her own.) There were morphine tablets, and oxygen masks, and insurance papers. What there weren't were long drawn-out goodbyes, movie deathbed scenes. My mother sat upright in bed with a red ribbon in her hair, transforming extraordinarily from a high priestess and queen in one moment to the little girl I felt she'd only gotten to be at the end of her life, a vulnerability from someone as controlling as she that was permitted only by a fatal illness.

She said, "You know how I feel about your lifestyle, and that's not going to change. But whomever you're with, you be your own man. Whether I agree with the decision you've made or not, I always wanted you and your sister to stand up for yourselves and be happy." Later that night, she called out to me because she was having trouble breathing and asked me told hold her hand as we said the 23rd psalm together. Looking at the fingers shaped like a claw around mine, I had the sudden memory of my mother breaking a piece of thread with her teeth and leaning over her sewing machine when I was six. She had spent days making a black Raggedy-Ann doll from scratch because she didn't want my sister, who was four, to have a white one.

Kids are stupid. They think if they squeeze their mommies tight enough they'll never leave them. They think as long as their mommies are in the world, they are safe. Now all I could think of was the profound mystery of death, which is always a cliché until someone you love dies. I felt as if someone had punched a hole in the sky and sucked my mother off the planet. The grief was so shattering that it was life-affirming in the end, a pain so awesome it couldn't be shopped or drunk or fucked away. When she was alive, I'd always known where to find my mother, even on those occasions when I was more than happy not to find her. Now I wondered, just on a practical level, where she was. No one knew that I had closed her casket when the wake was over and everyone had left. I was the last one to leave her in that cold room with the flowers and close air and heavy carpet. Before I lowered the lid, I said one last time, trying to voice my confusion at it all, "Mom?" My mother had always promised that if I ever called her, she would come. I had been sick often as a child, even hospitalized on several occasions because of my asthma, and during those times the softest "Mom?" would have my mother at my bedside with the thermometer or a Popsicle. As her eyes now stayed firmly shut, and her mouth, turned down at the sides in a final look of disapproval, didn't move, I knew she was gone. The woman from the funeral home had offered her condolences in that endless, silent corridor and handed my sister and me a box filled with my mother's ashes. The idea was absurd: I couldn't get my mind to agree that my mother was in that box. We thanked her, said goodbye and went home.

David Francey

John Wayne Rides East

Here we are in Los Angeles
There's lots of cars and tall palm trees
We found ourselves in a cobbled yard
Just off Ventura Boulevard
And I have to say that they treat you well
At the Tokyo Princess Motor Hotel.

She's sixty-five if she's a day
But she's beautiful in her own way
Her throne room is the check-out desk
Behind the sheets of plexiglass
But she'll smile and nod and wish you well
At the Tokyo Princess Motor Hotel.

And in a quirk of time and space
The Duke himself once ran this place
Before he tamed the wild west
He handed towels out to the guests
That's the story that they like to tell
At the Tokyo Princess Motor Hotel.

The Duke has taken his last ride
King Chai has crossed the ocean wide.

The Encino Inn in Marion's day
The trappings of the cowboy way
I guess he had some sheets to change
Before he changed his name to Wayne
He might have won the West
But you couldn't tell
By the Tokyo Princess Motor Hotel.

(Los Angeles, Ca. Oct. 16 2003)

Plastics Factory (8 Long Hours)

Open the door,
Take out the crate,
Close the door,
Press the button,
First machine, stamp the side,
Turn the crate, stamp the side,
Second machine, stamp the side,
Turn the crate, stamp the side,
Pick up the knife, clean the handles,
Turn the crate, clean the handles,
Stack the crate, on the pallet,
Turn around,
Open the door,
Take out the crate,
Close the door,
Press the button,

For eight long hours...

(February 9, 2002; Sceptre Manufacturing,
Scarborough, Ont. summer of '75.)

Working Poor

I run a genny on the back of my truck
And I take my chances
And I trust my luck
Well I may work tomorrow
But I can't be sure
I'm just a common example
Of the working poor.

I push a shovel on a building site
And I'm already working
When it breaks daylight
If I don't keep moving
Man, I'll freeze for sure
I'm just a common example
Of the working poor

I swing a hammer on a roof top high
I'll be swinging that hammer
On the day I die
I can raise your rafters
I can lay your floors
I'm just a common example
Of the working poor

I went to school until I had my fill
I was born in the shadow
Of the textile mill
Follow my father
To the factory floor
I'm just a common example
Of the working poor

(Words and Music: David Francey, [1983/94] SOCAN [1998])

Katherine Govier

Lie Down

(This story first appeared in Ars Medica.)

As soon as I heard, I called Maxine. And she said, if you want to join this deathwatch you are welcome.

I know it sounds bitter, but it wasn't really; it was just her vintage candor. I said, I will come to visit. What can I bring?

And Maxine said, *an explanation.*

Of all the old friends, some will be reconciled, with or without a prognosis of death. Of all the dead, some will lie down and others will not. Maxine will not. After being given eighteen weeks and no hope, she lasted eighteen months in a remission so convincing that people took her for a liar. It was embarrassing because a wake had been planned. She was a terrific organizer, and this got organized right back at her. The date was set, and the invitations were out. They were raising money for a memorial award in her name. Maxine not only lived to attend her wake, looking fabulous, and gave a fine speech, but she has continued to live right through the next winter. She's pretty funny on the subject. Now when certain names come up she says, "Oh yeah, Bill gave money and now he's mad at me because I didn't die. He thinks I'm faking."

For a while it did appear that Maxine wasn't dying after all, at least not on that particular speeded-up schedule. She was offered a counselor. But she emerged from the process claiming she'd been told she was doing so well in denial that she might as well stay there. We could be with her, but we couldn't have a say. We couldn't pity and we couldn't protest.

Maxine doesn't like being talked about and she doesn't like dying. I play by her rules, for now. Still, we both know she won't escape, much as she'd like to.

Outside a wind whips up the discarded donut wrappers and cigarette foil and makes them dance around tree trunks in front of the street-level window where I sit drinking coffee. A lot of sick people die just before spring. They make it through the winter but the warmth is so slow in coming they just wither.

People go by with their hands in their pockets and hair flying; they look in as if checking to see if I am real. For reasons not entirely within my control the city is for me a fish bowl. I signal for the bill: passersby take note. I push back my chair carefully. It reminds me of a certain e. e. cummings poem where he says spring is the hand in the window moving things but not breaking anything. I can identify with window dressing.

I leave the coffee shop and head down to her house. I'm going to take her out for lunch.

After that first call, I appeared, bringing a casserole. I had no *explanation* for the fact we'd fallen out of touch.

But I wasn't asked for one: Maxine let me off the hook. "We don't need to talk about all that, do we?" she said. I listened instead.

Pretty well my favorite phrase – and this has nothing to do with Celine Dion – is, *It's all coming back to me.* You know that wonderful rush you get when some big lost chunk of your life swings back into view? Hearing Maxine's caustic voice brought back the following: 1975, feeling sophisticated, eating Fettucine Alfredo at Luigi's beside the Morrissey, riding our bikes up Jarvis Street from our smart jobs in television. Discovering an actual outdoor cafe on Markham Street. Seeing Toronto Dance Theatre's nude males crawl out of black sacks on the lawn in front of Hart House. Always coming home to the third floor and calling The Answering Service for messages. Back then, there was no voice mail. This service was manned by out of work actors. "Hi there, did ya' have an okay day? A bunch of your friends called you," the star of tomorrow would say.

Maxine tells me that her tumor has reappeared, *(all coming back to me)*. The remission is over.

The news has made her angry. She insists, as she has before on occasion, that Rick, her ex-, gave her the cancer. She considers giving up. "A small sneaking part of me," she actually says, "welcomes the chance to lay down my responsibilities."

I listen. Once before she admitted to me that she was frightened. Only once. We talk about Auschwitz, why do people carry on? Hope, she says. Hope of a last minute rescue. And sometimes it comes.

When we first met, she'd had a miraculous recovery from a car accident. I walked into a party; she was there in two casts and propped up on pillows in a corner with various men dancing attendance. While she was still on crutches we had meal after cheap meal on Bloor, at the Blue Cellar, exchanging intimacies. Her place on Palmerston was just a block over from mine. There was a schnitzel joint we called "the Hungarian"; the owner was a tuberous giant of a man who we were convinced was a Nazi war criminal. Once a year he stood on each of the little tables in his restaurant, one after another, hanging Christmas tinsel from the ceiling. It was a terrible thing to watch him climb on those spindly-legged Formica numbers with screw-on aluminum legs. We feared the legs would give out, that he would topple, pulling down all the acoustic tiles into our breaded veal cutlets.

When people sink into illness their voices are the last thing to go. Hers is a bit raspy, surprisingly low for her tiny size. I could listen as long as she could talk. Certain remarks of hers, simple sentences uttered over nearly thirty years, stay with me as if the conversation took place only hours ago. "It was the real thing," she said of our friendship in a valedictory way when she considered our estrangement to be final. And, "You know I am on your side," once when a friend of hers made off with my serious lover. In the old days a group of us borrowed play sets from the Yorkville Library and did readings. I was always the ingénue. Maxine was the dowager.

"I guess you got that out of your system," I quipped on our last lunch.

She shot me a sharp glance. "I may have style but I do not mean to make this look easy." The dying are allowed to joke about it; we others are not.

From her bedside, my eyes rove to that sunshine that I can see paving the normally grey street with a line of purest yellow. Spring is a perhaps hand in a window, the

50

poet said, "carefully to and fro moving New and Old Things". Which are we? Not new but not yet old, each spring a tad more faded, but we do have style; spry does not yet apply. We are light and loose, compared to the heavy furniture of the aged. Perhaps we always will be, we of our group, who live on.

Although the hand does its stealthy damage. For instance, when did thus it arrange the free radicals and the cancer cells so delicately in Maxine's pancreas as to begin the slow destruction? No one saw. Perhaps for years no one knew. A year ago the disease blossomed; in summer it was mowed under; in winter it slept, and now with the season it wakes, ravenous.

She is tired. But she wants to come to lunch, so I help her dress. "Perhaps it's time to accept the inevitable," says Maxine, partway through getting the sweater on.

"Out of the question," I say. I put myself on the dream team from the start. "You'll see your fiftieth birthday," I say. "We're going to go to Mexico as soon as you're on your feet."

This too is a Toronto thing. Flight. I'm thinking I'll drive her down the highway that runs along the east coast. The A1A, it's called. It is a slow, two-lane highway that cars must share with bicycles. Driving, one is descended upon by flocks of aggressive cyclists with their lozenge-shaped, shiny, insect-like helmets. They swerve around you and curse and shake their fists so that you are glad air conditioning forces you to keep the windows rolled up.

I feel the lure of that road. When you get to the north of Florida you can turn off inland to Orlando. At Universal Studios there is a King Kong ride. An almost genial ape looms over the skyline and picks up the subway car you're riding in and threatens to peel it like a banana. Farther south the highway winds past the mansions of the very rich, and the stacked-up high-rise condominiums of the middle-class elderfolk who likewise flock there, and even past the trailer community of Briny Breezes, with its hair salon adorably called Briny Hair. The road is sometimes in sight of the beach, but more often the beach is hidden by wrought iron gates, golf clubhouses, town bathing pavilions and some of the few remaining natural dunes in the state. You can take this highway all the way to Miami, the Keys, to jump off for points south. I want to drive down it slowly, down, down to a place of easy long stupid days and no painful annual struggles to come back from the dead. Just me and Maxine and her intravenous.

We set off up the sidewalk heading for Bloor Street and lunch. Maxine wears a morphine-dispensing box on her side that she punches when she feels pain, and a colostomy bag under her overalls. Her post-chemo hair is a khaki ruffle like the feathers on a baby chick. Her feet are so swollen she can't wear shoes: they are stuffed into a pair of clogs. She clings to my arm and stumbles. She looks down at her legs as she walks and of course mine hove into view as well. "Your tights are navy," she says, "but you think they're black because you didn't look carefully."

At lunch she eats nothing. "You starve to death with this thing, that's what happens, did I tell you?" she says. She is so thin her spine stands out several inches from the flesh of her back and feels as hard as a row of nails. She wants me to touch it in the restaurant, just as, while she dressed, she wanted to show me the bag attached to her navel. She can't sit on chairs without cushions. In the sunlight I can see a fine white down on her face that is the same as the down my babies had when they were born, *lanugo*. When the morphine makes her lose the thread of the conversation she charges, "Bring me back!"

"Come back!" I say.

"I loved my body," she says.

I note the past tense.

She wants to talk about sex. She starts by telling me about a book written by a gay man, giving sex tips for women. "Don't bother with all that fancy stuff when you give a blow job," she says, "they just like it hard and deep." Her lover still climbs into bed with her: she needs to know that he desires her, that he is not put off by the bag of shit on her belly. Maxine avers that she has never been sure that men actually *liked* going down on women. But her lover now actually does. "It's a big mysterious organ and making it move gives him a sense of power," she says.

I remember this sex talk from the seventies. Penis size, predilections, who lasted longer. It stopped for a couple of decades. But we are at it again. Marriage, loyalty to the fathers of our children, dropped the curtain of silence on this subject. It will take more than husbands to shut Maxine down. She can say what she wants. She is facing the distinguished thing, as Edith Wharton calls death, quoting Henry James.

When I take her home she is exhausted and lies on her bed. She thumps her morphine purse angrily until finally she slides into another place from which I do not bring her back. I look at her closed eyes and tell her how strong and brave she is and how our friendship is the real thing and that I am on her side.

As I leave she raises her eyelids. "Next time we'll go

shopping to l'Elegance." That's a designer resale place on Yorkville. All her dresses are too big. She wants something smaller to be buried in. And will I take her for a facial and a body wax? Yes, I say. I'm pretty sure this will not happen. The nurse in charge of this campaign, Maxine's best – because we've arrived at the stage, finally, where people other than Maxine herself are in charge – will never allow it.

I walk downstairs and through her kitchen to the door. People are gathering, people who have been more consistent, people who never fell out, or who, I suppose, brought the explanations they were asked for. These custodians are talking about her fondly, marveling at her every gesture and word, as if she is, as if she *were*, a precocious child. I will not do it.

The wind whips my hair into my face as I say goodbye. I turn right and walk back up to Bloor. It happened while I was at her bedside; the wind took away the last of the cold. The half-concrete snow, that crust laced with black lay along the curb so long this year, has vanished. Spring is so short here. By the time she's gone a fine dust, the dust of summer, will be rising.

Robin Robinson

Getting A Grip

Call me non-observant but since turning 40 almost a dozen years ago, I have continued to think of myself as solidly "in my 40s" – suspended happily somewhere between hip and hip replacement. So it came as a surprise to discover recently I had left my mid-40s way behind.

Reality dawned sometime after my 51st birthday when I realized that all those news reports about aging Baby Boomers were talking about me. Born in 1955, I am part of the generation of excess that is, apparently, now poised to bankrupt the Canada Pension Plan and decimate the health care system as it marches in lockstep toward old age.

Had I been paying more attention, the signs were undeniable – the creaky knees, the silver "highlights", the crinkles – okay, wrinkles – around the eyes, even a mysterious allergic reaction that turned out to be a hot flash and gave new meaning to the term "hottie." I was definitely... getting older.

Like legions before me who have experienced this

sobering, small epiphany, it predictably triggered a lot of not very original mental machinations on the downside of aging. But somewhere along that dark path to despair, cynicism gave way to self ridicule over the futility of travelling down that twisted road.

My reasoning went like this: The only force that stops aging is death, so short of jumping into the abyss right now, it's not like we can do anything about it. So my advice to myself – and others worried about aging – is, get a grip.

A good place to start is by tuning out the psycho-babblers who make you feel as if time is running out. Self help gurus glibly talk about living in the moment as if it's humanly possible to live any other time. Today may be the only day we can seize, but this is the only moment we can live in.

But if we choose to not "make every moment count," opting instead for a nap on a Sunday afternoon or a glass of wine and a great novel on the deck, I say that's okay.

The truth is, my 20s and 30s were a whirl – not only a wonderful time of self discovery but also a time of angst and uncertainty. A time of turmoil over not knowing who I was or where I was going, of striving to balance raising a family and building a career, of always having too much to do and never having enough time to do it. In short, it was a time of vacillating between feelings of complete confidence and utter inadequacy.

Today, I may be considered past my prime but I know who I am and I can live with myself. And I know my companions on life's journey. I don't care nearly as much about what others think and – apart from family or professional obligations – I don't waste time doing things I don't like with people I don't enjoy. I spend time with people who matter – to me. I'm not trying to look hip or make an impression and I don't wear things that aren't comfortable. I don't feel like I have to save the world.

Like everyone, I have learned some hard lessons along the way. I have learned that people – even people I love – will surprise, delight and disappoint me by doing wonderful and horrible things. But the only person's thoughts, actions and reactions I can truly control are my own and that the lion's share of happiness comes from within.

I have also joined the legion of women past a certain age who can go almost anywhere unnoticed and unquestioned. Some people call this becoming invisible. I call it the cloak of anonymity and try to make it work for me by scooting past street people and sales people unmolested, or making a beeline to the shortest checkout line before other shoppers notice. I firmly believe middle aged women could have a very big future with Canada's spy agency.

Aging can be liberating from other perspectives, too.

If you were fortunate enough to have had children, you might be blessed with grandchildren. This is one of the least complicated, most joyful family relationships as someone else does the heavy lifting of parenting.

It's natural to think that becoming a grandparent might make you feel old but the truth is, it makes you feel young. Children reawaken your sense of fun by making it okay to act a little silly. They will remind you of your childhood, and your children's childhood and of a million happy family times. They are exhausting and challenging, and just when you feel you have spent every last bit of energy you have, they go home at the end of the day or weekend.

There are pluses on the fashion front, too. If you are a woman over 50 no one will ask you to wear a pink taffeta bridesmaid's dress, and you can say goodbye to sandals with ribbons that crisscross around the leg and tie in a bow, and opt instead for nice leather shoes that don't make you look like a birthday present. Ditto for pop tops, low slung jeans, puffy sleeves, ruffles, and other cutesy fashions you didn't feel comfortable in when you were 20 but felt compelled to wear.

A simple black skirt or well cut pants and a tailored blouse will take you almost anywhere in comfort and style, with your dignity intact. There will be no wardrobe malfunctions.

In case you haven't noticed, once you hit 50 most of the movers and shakers, the law makers and law enforcers. are younger than you. Instead of feeling passed over, I prefer to embrace the notion that I have been freed from doing some of the really hard jobs in life.

Our society has low expectations for people over 50. It's generally accepted that we ruined the world, so no one expects us to fix it.

Those brilliant young people following fast in our footsteps think they have all the answers, and – who knows – maybe they do. They want to make the hard choices, run the country and solve the world's ills.

I say, let them.

We can still do our small part for charity, for conservation, for the arts, etc., but those energetic youths can lose sleep pondering the really big questions.

Yes, we are marching toward old age and inevitable death. But so far, we have not succumbed to tragic accidents, suicide, early cancers, drug addictions, heart attacks, brain aneurisms, and a litany of other ills that have taken dear friends and beloved family members too young.

Our stars may soon be setting, but for now we are still of the universe. We are the survivors – of broken hearts and failed dreams, of lost friendships and lost loves. Our outsides may be sagging but inside we're pure steel.

And that is not to be mourned but to be celebrated.

Paul Knowles

I May Not Know Art, But...

How much art can you buy for $176.03? Including tax?

This is, of course, a question that haunts art-lovers everywhere. Which raises a second question: "What, exactly, is an art-lover?" To quote John Cleese, artfully playing the part of the Pope to Eric Idle's Michelangelo (albeit a Michelangelo who has unfortunately produced a "Last Supper" including dozens of apostles, three Christs, a bevy of waiters and a kangaroo... where was I?)

Oh, yes: Pope Cleese, after abjuring this blasphemous work, declared, "I may not know art, but I know what I like."

As for me, I definitely do not know art; sometimes, I am also not at all sure what I like.

I did, however, very much like the painting I saw at an art auction exhibition in Toronto. And owing to having friends in higher places than I normally inhabit, I was able to get up close and personal with it: Tom Thomson's "Burnt Area with Ragged Rocks", an 8 1/2 by 10 1/2 inch (if Tom Thomson didn't go metric, why should I?) mini-masterpiece hanging in the preview to a Sotheby's auction of "Important Canadian Art."

There was plenty of impressive art in the room, including paintings by A.Y. Jackson, Emily Carr, A.J. Casson, Lawren Harris and Jean-Paul Riopelle. Okay, just to prove my point that I don't, in fact, know art, I hereby confess that I don't "get" Riopelle. Even now, as I flip through the Sotheby's catalogue and consider the four Riopelles that were on offer in that sale, I get nothing. Nadda. They're worth seven figures, some of them. On a good day, I might be able to afford three figures to the left of the decimal point (see $176.03, above) and would not even spend that much on a Riopelle.

So I stand exposed as an art imbecile.

None the less, I loved the Thomson. It was a thing of beauty, especially the section which the catalogue writer – clearly inspired – described as "a sky that is a miracle in paint." Yes, it was.

When I see a painting that good, that wonderful, that... well, clearly desirable... I want it just as much as the next guy. The only difference being that, at a Sotheby's preview, most of the next guys actually have the money to buy such a painting. The pre-auction estimate was between $150,000 to $250,000. That proved to be something of an underestimate – the Thomson went for a final price that was near $1 million. That's something over $11,000 per square inch.

I tend to leave events such as the Sotheby's preview just a tad depressed. I don't claim to understand the art, but there are some paintings that just cry out to be loved, and I can love them as well as anyone, except I clearly don't have the bank balance for that kind of cultural romance.

Artistically speaking, I have resigned myself to the perpetual role of spurned suitor. Well, no – I'll never even make it to the "suitor" stage. When it comes to great art auctions, I'm more like the guy standing across the street from a church as the wedding party emerges, who then goes and gets a cheap massage from a beefy woman who has long since seen her 60th birthday. Too much imagery? Sorry.

As it turned out, all was not lost in my quest to acquire art. In my rather masochistic exploration of art auction internet websites, I found an auction house in London, Ontario, which seemed to be offering art at considerably less cost than Sotheby's or its tony Toronto counterparts.

In particular, the upcoming auction featured several paintings that actually seemed quite desirable. So, accompanied by my best friend and companion, I went to the auction house in question to preview the works.

Many of the paintings that seemed appealing on-line were quickly dismissed in person. As were a couple of works that bore the signatures of some of the famous painters named above, although the paintings clearly were not from the sources indicated by the faux signatures. But there were two pieces that especially interested us: an English water colour – a lovely thing, a typical misty English scene of meadow and river – and an oil painting. The oil was a Laurentian Shield scene by a reputable Canadian artist named Stuart Clifford Shaw (1896-1970) – it was a bit Group-of-Sevenish at a tiny fraction of a Group-of-Seven price. More Group of Six Thousand, perhaps.

My b.f. and c. could not attend the actual auction with me, so I convinced a buddy to accompany me. He owes me – I once helped him carry out an illicit after-hours entry into a boat repo yard in order to check out the marine merchandise, not that I would ever admit to such activities, of course.

So he came along to offer moral support, and also – given my extremely limited resources – to stop me from doubling or tripling my intended maximum bid, always a danger when I am at an auction. He had his bid-prevention tactics at the ready, including arm-wrestling and ripping up my bidding card.

The first painting, the water colour, came up early in the day. I was right ready to bid, and I had set my limit at a reasonable level. I sat, poised, as two rude, nasty, pushy people in the front part of the room offered instantaneous competing bids, carrying the price far beyond my limit, and well above the auctioneer's estimate. Eventually, one of them got the water colour. I had not managed to even register a bid.

My friend said, "Too bad. That's how it goes." I must say, his lack of sympathy rankled. But all unawares, he continued, "When does your other piece come up?"

I checked. It was about 150 numbers down the list; they were auctioning about one item a minute.

"Lots of time for food," said my friend, and we wandered out into downtown London in search of a warm room and a decent menu. An hour later, well fortified with omelets, we sauntered back to the auction. The oil painting I wanted was still more than an hour away, by the numbers, so I sat back to relax. I certainly wasn't going to bid on anything else.

Up came an intriguing item. A mahogany, serpentine

credenza, was how I think it was described. Anyway, it was quite lovely, and certainly old.

The bidding began, and stayed relatively low, for a while.

"Yes, I have the bid from the gentleman seated at the side, near the back."

Hey, I was seated at the side, near the back. I looked at my friend, who had his hand in the air.

"You may have to lend me your bidding number," he whispered out of the side of his mouth..

"What are you doing?" I asked.

"It's a nice piece. And I'm bored," he answered.

He got the credenza, and registered it to my number. Before the oil painting I wanted came up, he also managed to bid on several other items, and picked up a small Tiffany tea urn, a gift for his wife.

Finally, we got to my oil painting. You know you are in trouble at an auction, by the way, when before the bidding has even begun you come to think of the object as "mine." That tends to cause utter abandonment of reason. And so it went – as with the other painting I had coveted, the bids went up, well beyond the published estimate, and well above my firm maximum bid. But finally, it was sold. To me. Because my buddy was by now so distracted, trying to figure out what else he might like to buy, that I was able to slip the bonds of reason and restraint that he had placed on me, and bid way over my head.

Over my head being a relative term, of course – I was still safely within the three-figure range.

I brought the painting home; its presence caused the rearrangement of the art on the parlour walls. I use the term "art" in the broadest of senses, to include anything just slightly more elegant than a decorative wall calendar. At least, I don't think there were any wall calendars in the parlour. If there were, they were permanently removed in the artistic redistribution.

But I also brought home a bit of useful knowledge. At the auction, there had been an announcement – well, more of a vague hint – that some evening soon, there would be an art-only auction, as this particular establishment cleared out its attics and closets.

And you see, the acquisition of the Shaw oil painting had unleashed the collector that lurked within. I had originally abandoned all hope of acquiring nice paintings by Thomson or Carr – somewhat inhibited by a complete lack of funds – but now, I realized that obtaining some original art for my walls might be doable. Not great art, perhaps, but original, and, most importantly, mine. Such is the obsession of the infected collector.

I started to check the website regularly, and before long, the announcement appeared: Art auction, in London, on a Monday evening.

I consulted with my b.f. and c., who agreed to accompany me, determined, I am sure, to be more effective than my buddy had proved to be in keeping me within reasonable bidding parameters.

We arrived early, to preview the art to be auctioned. There were 360 lots – some of them including up to a dozen paintings, prints, and etchings. That's a whole lotta' art. We toured the collection, noting those which we might think would look nice in my parlour, at least until a Tom Thomson comes along.

We identified 50.

Fifty! We went around again, and then a third time, narrowing the field, winding up with a list of about six that we thought were worth consideration. If the price was right. Said price being monitored carefully by my b.f. and c., sitting beside me, holding the reins tightly, and the bidding card in her other hand.

The seats were only about half full, and it soon became clear that some of those in attendance were there because there is not a lot of entertainment in downtown London on a Monday evening. So the real field of bidders numbered no more than 20. Twenty bidders, for 360 lots, maybe 500 pieces of art.

Ah, gentle reader, you have perhaps perceived the outcome. We started cautiously, really we did, marshalling our forces for the first piece we hoped to buy. And yes, we got it, outbidding a dealer to pick up a genuine, old oil painting by Z. Massclus (or maybe Masselus? We can't tell) for only $60.

Soon after that came a an intriguing little oil painting of a cabin in winter. It was signed – by whom, I'm not sure. But it was a nice painting, and if it were to go cheap, I might be interested. It did, in fact, go cheap – for $5. To me.

The floodgates had opened. They were not to close again until the auctioneer knocked down lot 360 (which I did not buy; heck, I hadn't purchased a painting since lot 356). Came the reckoning. We were now the proud owners of 35 original oils, watercolours, and a print or three that had been included in job lots.

Not everyone, of course, collects paintings by the square meter, but that was apparently to be our approach.

The car was loaded from its guggle to its zatch, but we got the paintings home. Well – most of them. My best friend and companion had judiciously discarded a couple of bullfighter prints and one or two other items from job lots behind a post in the auction room, so we really came home with about 30 works of art. The bill? Ah, you already know — $176.03, including tax, and buyers' premium.

Arriving chez moi, we lugged the art into the parlour. We may not know art, but we knew, even in the cold light of gluttonous acquisition, that we liked a lot of these pieces. The sorting began.

As I write, seven of those paintings, all originals, hang in my parlour. Some we actually have learned something about — a watercolour by Northern Ontario artist Jack Lockhart, a large oil by post-war immigrant artist Otto Grebze. Others are signed or initialed, but the signatures are so far indecipherable.

It does not stop there. More of the paintings hang in the kitchen; some are in my bedroom; one is in the foyer. Two are now in my son's apartment, since his attitude was, "free art is better than no art." Wonder where he got that idea?

Some have been jettisoned; a few languish in the basement, awaiting a later verdict.

With the new stuff added to the Shaw and a couple of paintings by my old friend, the late artist Matthew Kousal, my parlour is now completely decorated with original works.

Perhaps the most intriguing painting of the lot is the one apparently signed "Z. Massclus". In an odd turn of events, I had the chance to have it evaluated by the president of Sotheby's of Canada. My buddy — he who purchased the unexpected serpentine credenza — called to inform me that said Sotheby's official had dropped by, and would I care to meet him?

I arrived within minutes, painting in hand, ready, willing and eager to take advantage of this opportunity. The Sotheby's personage – the same man who wrote the "miracle in paint" comment about the Tom Thomson landscape – considered my painting, said, "It's a nice little painting. Never heard of Massclus, though. Too bad."

Well, maybe he knows art... but I know what I like. And what I like is paying $176.03 for a houseful of art. No Tom Thomsons, of course, but by my calculation I have saved $999,823.97. Less two omelets, plus tip.

Barbara Kingstone

Whatever Happened to Modesty?

If I hadn't been there myself, standing in the buff, like the day I was born, I would never have believed it.

Marrakech's legendary hotel, La Mamounia, is noted for many things – glorious art deco lobby, signature art deco furniture, trickling mosaic fountains, magnificent gardens, poolside restaurants and other fine gourmet eateries. It's also the hotel where Winston Churchill came for an R &R and now there's a continuous roster of celebs who frolic in this colorful Moroccan city. La Mamounia also has a spa.

The first hint that perhaps my skin was in need of some attention was completely due to one of the many hotel amenities – a loofah mitt. No big deal, I thought then, but this was a mitt with wow power. Sloughing the dead cells left my skin silky. So now I was on a roll about my epidermis. I booked an appointment for the hotel's hammam (a steam bath) with all the trimmings.

It was a hot, sticky day, I had done the Souk (a vast market place) in the morning, spent mucho dirhams here and there helping out the local economy, and now all I wanted to do was get as far away from the city's sensory overload of dust, crowds and consumer temptations. I wanted to de-stress and be pampered.

Down I went to this model of marble splendor. A long, narrow reflecting pool stretching the full length of the area with intermittent crossovers was where a large-ish woman dressed in nurse's white met me. She spoke as much English as I did Arabic. In other words – none. However, she must have gotten the drift of my queries from my hand signals because I was led into a small locker room where she motioned for me to take off everything.

I had come from my room, through the elegant lobby wearing the fluffy hotel-provided terry bathrobe trimmed with Mamounia pink, and in my Canadian modesty, wearing a bathing suit underneath, and real shoes. None of those fuzzy slippers in public for me.

So here I was – undressed, my minimal clothing neatly hung in a smart looking wooden locker which would later take me 15 minutes to open. With the constant stream of moisture, these small storage areas were all warped; hence, stuck.

Large Woman handed me an oversized towel, which I quickly wrapped, high pareo style, around myself. Large Woman pointed to a door and when I entered, there was a hunk of a man wearing wet, tight biking shorts, showering down another female guest. In a state of disbelief and frankly, astonishment, I felt like a voyeur at a porno palace as he stretched her arms, rinsing them from wrist to armpit then washed down the front and back and every fold known to the female human form.

My first and only thought was, is this going to happen to me and how do I disappear without anyone noticing? The perfect time for a floor to open. But there was no escape. I had to save face.

Josef (I only learned his name when we became fairly close to each other!) told me to shower using only water, no soap — yet. So far so good. But not for long. Just wishful thinking and a small prayer.

After my fellow hammam-ite departed for cooler and less invasive spa areas, it was now my turn. Not only was I losing face fast, but also my modesty. Josef suddenly took a handful of a thick olive oil paste mixture, which he proceeded to smear on my entire body, leaving only my neck and face exempt from this goo. Was it just for my comfort when he told me it will make me sweat and that stuff will disappear while I'm the steam? It did, as did my ego.

Still in shock, I stayed in the marble steam-filled room where I serendipitously put on the wooden-soled shoes provided for the clients. Luckily, a wise move, since the floor was like a furnace, as was the marble bench. Another bit of quick thinking was to have brought my towel, which had become my security blanket. After 15 minutes, or so, Josef retrieved me from this cloudy mist-filled oven of a room. And the fun began, on a low bench covered with smart tooled red leather cover, this being Morocco and all, so an appropriate accessory. Josef then layered a towel on top of the leather, but not me, and I was told to lie on my back.

When I had left the hammam just minutes before, my face was flaming red. Now, I had become ashen as I stretched out, nude as the day I was born and not one part of me covered except a shower cap for my hair. The scrub began and though I should have been flinching, I began feeling very Zen, taking myself away from here. Zone out time. From the toes to the neck, Josef didn't miss a body part. Then, like a rotisserie chicken, I was asked to turn over and same schpiel, yet again. By now, I was totally immune to everything, and the only option was to speak to Josef until this so called de-stress session was over.

Josef was born and raised in Marrakech. Hammams and exfoliating are part of the culture, he tells me. When he's not de-sloughing, a chic Chicago guest later told me over drinks (I needed one very badly), he works as a private masseur – and a well respected and mighty good one too.

"Sit up," he said and I obeyed immediately. Now face to face, he got right into my shoulders, back and chest and yes, boobs. Just as fast as it was done, I was back into the first room where, with complete trepidation, I was showered exactly as the former client had been.

And for the finale, I was handed lotion, which I started to apply only to have Josef continue the spreading. I was grateful that it was soon hosed off with a strong stream of luke warm water.

In my investigative mode, afterward, I searched out the first woman I had "met" and ask her opinion about this somewhat intimate session. Without a pause, she admitted she loved it almost as much as the afterglow that came along with this abrasive rubdown.

In retrospect, she was right. My skin felt like a baby's bottom with a nice baby pink glow. I still haven't made a decision whether it had been worth the somewhat unusual, humbling experience. But for Josef, it's all in a day's work. Nothing personal. All that for only 350 dinhars (about $50) and a self-help ego boosting session, to boot.

David Hobson

Beyond the Outback

It's 1985 and I'm in Australia, driving north to Alice Springs along the Stuart Highway, searching for a dream. Highway? It isn't paved. It isn't even graded. It's known as The Track, an excuse for a road that's used mostly by road trains: multi trailer trucks loaded with cattle, racing south to beat the heat. The surface is corrugated by the trucks and I soon discover that thirty four mph seems to be the optimum speed that keeps the reverberations of my old car to a steady rumble, although the optimum speed for a road train appears to be about 80 mph. Where the road isn't rippled hard like a washboard, it's covered in a thick layer of dust, the colour and texture of paprika. It swirls behind the road trains as they chase the horizon shimmering in the distance.

Every time a truck roars by, my car is enveloped in a rusty mist. The dust settles in the pot holes and large depressions and as my old car plunges into these pools of silence, the creaks of the tortured suspension are muffled, creating a brief feeling of confidence in its reliability, only to have it shattered as I'm ambushed by yet another malicious cattle grid. These lie like abandoned tombstones, around a bend or over a rise, where they perform the dual purpose of ripping off a muffler and marking its final resting place.

Meanwhile, the scene through the windshield is a kindergarten watercolour, the page split between a blue sky and a red earth, with a big yellow sun and a few faint patches of faded green. As I drive north to the Alice, it hardly changes, hour after hour.

I've left civilization behind – if you can call Coober Pedy civilized. It's a worn out mining town, a last frontier kind of town where men still probe the earth for flashes of colour, opal junkies seeking a vein. The veins are never large enough, but the miners continue to tunnel their lives away, burying their dreams behind them.

My dream is that my car will survive the next hit and I'll stay on the road, although there's no ditch and nothing to hit, except perhaps an abandoned car that wasn't worth the price of a tow. Like everything else that dies out here, cars are soon picked clean by scavengers. I can't help noticing that many of the vehicles are of the same make and model as the one I'm driving, a '71 Holden wagon. It was recommended because of the wide availability of parts that litter the outback. I bought the car in Sydney – only $700 – a cash advance on my strained credit card. I hope to sell it when I return – if it survives the Stuart Highway.

When I filled up with gas back in Coober Pedy, at the station with the sign that said Last Petrol for Two Hundred Miles, I'd figured a full tank would easily make it but I can see the needle on the gas gauge is already sidling up to the red E much sooner than expected – definitely sooner than Alice Springs. I'm hot, tired and hungry, thinking that if I run out of gas, there'll be one more Holden on junkyard strip. Then, just by chance, as I glance in the rear-view mirror, I spot what looks like a cut off near the last corner I rounded. I would never have noticed it had I not glanced up at that very moment.

I turn the car round and drive back to the corner. Sure enough, it's an old dirt track intersecting at the bend in the road. It isn't marked on my map, but there is a small sign a little way in that proclaims, with outback honesty, "Grub and Gas – Maybe – 10 miles." My choices are limited – take a chance and drive down the track or stay on the road knowing that road trains can't or won't stop for me. I take the track thinking it might lead to a sheep station or mining settlement.

Nine miles in the engine begins to cough and wheeze, only to die completely as I clear the brow of a low hill. I coast into town – what there is of it – maybe a dozen abandoned buildings slumped together, all with red stone walls and rusty tin roofs, corrugated like the highway. Right in the middle stands a solitary gas pump, one of those old ones with a hand crank and a glass reservoir on top. It's alone and untended; hardly a beacon of hope to a lost traveller.

I get out and look around. The place has to be deserted. I cross the street to the closest building, the one with the sign that says "Rooms" I push open the door and enter, and I'm immediately hit by a blast of cool air. The contrast is a shock, but no more than my surprise and amazement to find someone sitting behind an office counter watching TV.

"Welcome, welcome. Sit yourself down," smiles the man. "Have a beer," he says, reaching into the refrigerator beside him. "I'm just watching this old Ed Sullivan rerun"

I join him – there isn't much else I can do. Finally the show comes to an end, with an encore by Topo Gigio, and the old man stands. He's tall and carrying a little extra weight, and he's dressed in black pants and a crisp white shirt. His face, worn by the sun and textured like old barn board is dark, but his thick hair and beard are pure white. He's a black and white negative.

"I just love those old shows," he grins. "Entertainment just ain't the same no more. Anyways, welcome to the Quality Hotel. Guess you'll be wanting gas. Most folks do that happen to find my place. Got a room if you want to stay the night. Old fashioned service – an' the food is pretty good too. I cook it myself. By the way, you can call me John."

"Sure, thanks," I say. I'm not likely to get a better offer.

He leads the way into the dining room. It's surprisingly spotless. The decor is early fifties; an old Wurlitzer stands in the corner. "Want some music?" he asks. "There's a good variety, great stuff from the fifties left behind when the place was first abandoned." He pulls a handful of change from his pocket and slaps it into my hand. "Take your pick. I gotta get my apron on. I'll be back in a minute." I choose a Buddy Holly number, Peggy something. Not my era, but I may as well relax and get into the mood.

And I do relax; my anxiety about getting lost in the outback is fading. The place has a feeling of serenity about it, yet I can't imagine how anyone could live so far from life. Through the window the street is windswept and empty. Beyond the gas pump is the same kindergarten landscape I've been looking at since I left Coober Pedy at dawn. It never ends. When the old guy returns I ask him what attracted him to this isolation. He just laughs.

"We'll talk later," he said. "Now, what are you going to eat? – I recommend the stewed lamb chops and potato dumplings followed by Pavlova for dessert. Might just have a nice bottle of '79 from the Barossa Valley in my wine cellar, if you'd like. I'll bring that right out."

He returns shortly with the bottle, pulls the cork with a sommelier's flourish and offers me a taste before returning to the kitchen. The wine is smooth, and after a few sips I relax even more. A wine cellar, beneath this shack of a place, miles from anywhere? I decide that I'm dreaming, and I don't care. It's the aroma that pulls me awake. A heaping plate is on the white table cloth before me. I eat. It's simple food, but so, so good. Then it's Australia's renowned dessert – Pavlova. I'm in the dining room of the gods.

John brings me coffee shortly and invites me out onto the back porch to watch the sun go down.

"Simple pleasures," he remarks, as he conjures up an almost empty bottle and a pair of glasses. "We'll share a small one," he chuckles. "I've made this last for years. An old Napoleon ain't something to be gulped at one sitting. It's quality stuff." I agree. Everything I've experienced over the last few hours has been quality stuff and I tell him so.

"Just doing the right thing," he says, "quality over quantity." Then he tells me his story.

"First came by here in the early seventies," he begins. "I was just touring around with a bunch of friends at the time, raising hell. We'd been drinking and partying and it was late. None of us knew where the heck we were or what we were doing. Things were never too clear in those days for any of my group. I just happened to mosey off and darned if I didn't get lost. I was out there in the desert for days, jus' wandering around. The boys thought I'd left town on my own, so they left too. By the third morning I got the feeling nobody was looking for me. Why would they? I was worth more dead than alive. Funny thing is I ain't scared. I jus' seemed to focus on what's going on around me. It's amazing how much there is to see when there's nothing else to do but look. You know, the desert looks dead at first glance, but life is real intense here when you learn how to see it.

"Anyways, I'm getting to thinking I'm close to the end of mine when this aborigine kid finds me. He's out there wandering around too – goin' walkabout he calls it, 'cept he could have wandered around for a month with nothing but his hands in his pockets – if he'd a had pockets. Me, with all my money and resources is about to check out. That kid brought me grubs to eat – grubs, not grub, mind you, and he brought me wet roots to suck on. Now that's quality food. He saved my life. When you've been that close it makes you think – a lot. It was like I just relearned something I used to know as a kid. Like I'd come home to something that seemed right.

"I call it quality. You know, quality of life. I decided to stay. My toy box had been fit to bust for some time and jus' didn't give me pleasure no more. I could see the good life was killing me and I didn't like the look of the future. I cashed in all I could and simply bought up what was left of the town. Now here I am, finding pleasure in giving the best of old fashioned, top quality service to the occasional traveller who happens by."

It's only when I ask him about family that a cloud comes over his face. "They couldn't come," he answered. "They couldn't let go of the quantity. I still keep in touch – kind of."

We sit quietly for a while, watching the sun put a fresh coat of paint on the biggest sky I've ever seen.

"You know," he says, breaking the silence, "The sun don't go down; we're racing away from it at a thousand miles an hour. Jus' a matter of perception, like things aren't always what they seem, nor what we want them to be."

He stands and goes inside, returning with a guitar. He sits back, puts up his feet, and begins to play. His voice is rich. It weaves in and out through the colours of the sunset, then as the sky in the east turns a deep indigo, it falls into a perfect harmony. I'm captivated.

"Did you write those songs?" I ask when he's finished.

"Kind of. I guess I had a little help from God. He's the real creator you know. But since we're made in his image, I create the best way I know how. He jus' gives me all the notes."

"How do you mean?" I ask, curious.

"See those stars up there? Every one of those stars is a musical note put there by God. I just pick out the ones I need."

"You could make a fortune with those songs you know; they're perfect."

"Make a fortune!" he snorted, "And then what? No, I'm happy to play for myself, or whoever wants to listen. It's enough for me, and speaking of enough, the day has been long enough for me. I'll show you your room, then wish you goodnight, son."

Like the rest of the hotel, the room is clean and simple, with a comfortable bed. As John says before he leaves, "It's no more or no less than a weary traveller needs."

I sleep well, and rise early, more rested than I've ever been. At my door I find a note telling me I can find coffee waiting in the dining room. I take a mug and sit on the porch, watching the sun rise. The air is still and the rays of light are soft, but I know that in this country, any promise the sun makes at dawn will be broken before noon when it turns ruthless.

I go to the office to pay my bill. The old guy won't hear of it. "I don't need your money, son." he chuckles, "Don't have any use for it. Let's get that car of yours filled up. You'll be wanting to leave."

I'm not sure I do, but we walk out to the pump together. He checks the oil and the tires, then cleans the windshield. Finally, he fills my gas tank. That is, he half fills it.

"I'd feel better if it you'd fill it right up," I suggest nervously.

"Fill it right up!" he snorts. "You don't need it full, son. You're too focused on the quantity. This is quality gas, finest gas in two hundred miles, guaranteed to take you to the Alice. What more could you want?"

I realize I have no reason to doubt him. We shake hands. "Thanks again," I say.

"You're welcome, son. Be on your way. An' when you think of me – think about quality."

As I drive off he yells out, "Don't look back, son. Don't ever look back."

But as I reach the top of the hill I just have to take a quick glimpse in the rear-view mirror. He's gone, of course. The place again looks deserted, but I know there is life down there, hiding away from the brutal glare of the midday sun.

I reach the Highway and head north, rumbling along to Alice Springs on my quality gas, thinking a quality highway wouldn't be a bad thing. I go on to travel the Northern Territory and Queensland, seeing people and things that TV can never make real. By the time I return to Sydney the car is only running on three cylinders. It's a wreck, and it's never really been mine, but it has fulfilled a dream for me, and I'm able to sell it in time to cover the payment on my credit card, yet I'm beginning to understand what the old guy meant.

The car had quality and it never let me down. That old guy had really believed in quality, right down to his shoes, the strangest shoes to be wearing in the outback. Naturally, they were covered in a layer of red dust, like everything else, but when he'd been filling the gas I'd accidentally stepped on his toe, scuffing the surface, only to see that underneath the dust his shoes, quality shoes, were blue – blue suede.

Lorna Crozier

Transplanted

This heart met the air. Grew in the hours
between the first body and the next
a taste for things outside it: the heat
of lights, their high intensity; snicks of sleet
across a window screen, the indifferent
kiss of fog or was it steam wafting from
the hot dog vendor's cart
on the street below? Often it skips

a beat – a head explodes the windshield,
a mare drops her womb-slick colt
in falling snow, a face the heart once knew
weeps in the corridor that gives nothing back
but unloveliness and glare.

Like a shovel as it hits the earth, then rises,
and hits the earth again, it feels its own dull blows
and knows there is an end to them. Some nights
it is a sail billowing with blood, a raw fist punching.
Some nights, beneath the weight of blankets,
bones and flesh, it remembers. Feels those
rubber gloves close around it, and goes cold.

Facts

Did you know the ant has a tongue,
the female mouse, a clitoris? I learned this from two poets –
one famous and American,
the other a student of biology and physics.

Now anything is possible:

Did you know that grass has legs and feet?
That's why it's never still
but runs on the spot like a child in an old gymnasium.

Did you know the moon cleans itself with a tongue
rough as a cat's? It licks and licks until it disappears
then comes up new again, shiny with spittle.

Did you know the yellow butterflies that feed on
cabbage
have a temper; the winds, a worrying mother?

Every dusk she stands in the airy doorway of the
world
and calls them home.

83

Getting Used to It

Our love making that day was slow and tender
as if both our childhoods crowded around our bed.
My mother, on her own now fourteen years,
had phoned. Her brother's widow two doors down
was having family over, but not her. "It's okay,"
Mom said. "I'm used to being treated this way,"
then, "Happy New Year," her loneliness
a hard salt on my skin. You moved over me like
water,
old water I'd swum in for years, knowing where
the bottom fell away, where warmth became a shiver,
then warmth again, you let me weep, you left
your smell all over me as if you'd first walked
naked in our garden, juniper, rosemary, snow's
bluest flowers melting on your skin, our bodies
old, now one year older. I swear I won't get used to
this,
your cries muffled in my hair, the hurt and no-one-
touching
that my mother has to bear; a thousand miles
away from us, a single setting at her table
this first day of her eighty-eighth new year.

Amanda Boyden

Dancing With the Fat Lady

Johanna scratched the sweat-damp lace of her new stretch bra. It was not hers, this city; she had been transplanted. She should have gotten out of the Quarter hours ago. Now she was stuck on Royal behind a beige diesel Mercedes, with both her car's temperature and gas gauges sneaking into red zones. Certainly New Orleans heat was the reason, the reason why the thing had grown like a mushroom in the Black Forest, a tadpole in a backyard pond, bread mold on agar. In their city, humidity clung to the heat; mildew in shower stalls devoured grout; ferns flourished without soil, stuck to the stone sides of downtown buildings. Everything in New Orleans grew too fast, unnaturally, turned green in hours, furtive as kudzu. Johanna's thing had seemed to grow overnight, had made her think the underwire of her old bra had punched through the satin. Just a little lump, a garbanzo bean, a fresh pea, a tiny turtle egg. But it was there under her soapy fingers in the shower three days ago.

The Quarter perspired. The smell of rotting garbage eddied sluggishly in the streets. The thing wanted to grow; it loved the climate, drank her sweat, ate her sweet breast flesh like manna.

The appointment was tomorrow. Johanna had been drinking too much in anticipation of the labeling, the medical umpire's call. She was feeding the lump yeast and barley and hops at regular intervals, spending her week off in Quarter corners, meeting waitress friends for long, drink-filled afternoons, and speaking French carelessly, forgetting tenses and articles. Her table-waiting companions didn't know; she had covered carefully. She had no one to tell.

The Mercedes inched forward. Johanna turned on her car heater, hoping to pull some of the heat away from the engine and into the interior. Might as well make the lump happy in its pre-inspected state. A noise, a clattering roar getting louder, started somewhere in the back of Johanna's head. Was she fainting? They would find her with steam billowing from under the hood of her car in the middle of the street. She would be slumped in her bucket seat, a sweaty palm clutching her small mound of breast with its inherited misfortune beneath her shirt.

The noise was outside her head. A mule was running wild with his carriage.

The female driver shouted, "Jessie, Jessie! Hoah...JESSIE!" Johanna turned and scraped her neck on the shoulder strap of her seat belt. The contraption of animal and metal and cloth and human barreled over the curb, raced crookedly down Royal, thundered past Johanna's car, and nicked the front fender of the Mercedes with a hard wheel. Jessie's small driver had lost the reins and rode in her seat like a drunk, like Johanna on her bar stool two nights ago, all alone, leaning, stunned, ashen. The driver's voice screeched.

Johanna knew Jessie didn't care about the street lamps, about the pedestrians, about the thing he was dragging behind him that screamed and hurt his muscles and ears.

Johanna heard Jessie and his driver crash in the next block. Johanna got out of her car and stood on her tiptoes, trying to see over the head of Mr. Mercedes, around the jammed traffic. Jessie had cleared the way. A space grew, and Johanna, deciding what must have happened, got back in her car and took it; she steered quickly around the gawkers, made a right turn from the left side of the Mercedes onto Conti. She was as free as Jessie. Away, away.

Johanna wanted to do something that night. Anything. Do anything and drink.

She would eat oysters with tabasco and lemon, listen to really loud music in a dive of a club, dance and talk to the old lost ladies out on the street, pick up a hitchhiker with the wrong colored skin and give him money straight from her wallet, give him a glimpse of all the starchy bills inside fresh from the ATM. She would fuck a find of a one-night-stand.

Friday's entertainment section said Jerry Lee Lewis met Salvador Dali at Muddy Waters that night, in a band from Athens, Georgia. Hillbilly Frankenstein was exactly what Johanna wanted, their name being what she had felt like for half a week. She would take up smoking, buy a pack of Marlboro reds. She would do shots of bourbon and send extras to the doorman and bartenders and good-looking band members. She would forget her chick pea for a few hours, let one of the happy drink recipients find it under the covers late at night, around four perhaps. He would kiss it, frown in the dark, not say anything, hope Johanna had a submerged third nipple she was too embarrassed to mention. She would wear her glitter dress and wiggle like an eel out on the dance floor.

In the Uptown club, her big black T-shirt absorbed the lights and tented her secret. Johanna wore striped leggings with red Doc Martins, her clumpy Olive Oyl boots. They always loved her long, muscled, wicked-witch gams. Those she could show off, display for her audience. She paid cover and walked to the bar.

The bartender came to her quickly. His eyes hovered around Johanna's mouth.

They always loved her big lips. She thought that her lips reminded them of their city, of magnolia cones ripening magenta, of things growing and blooming and swelling, lush, fat, and full. His eyes moved to the pale mole on her cheek, back to her mouth, over her smooth hair, rested at an earring. "Yes?" he asked.

"I don't know. Have a suggestion for the evening?" An idea, a plan, a drink special? Johanna tugged at the sleeve of her T-shirt. Her lump felt cramped.

"Ah, a victim," he said. "How 'bout a Hurricane, or one of the other disaster drinks? No? Bud pitchers are on special. So are burgers. A good medium rare with swiss maybe?"

"Thanks. A shot of rail bourbon and a Bud pitcher chaser, please."

"My kinda woman," the bartender said, turning his back, reaching for a shot glass.

"Grab two of those, why don't you. Join me, all right?" Johanna opened her purse and pulled out crumpled dollar tips. All her clothes, all her money, smelled of restaurant sour mix and rum, mesquite smoke and yams. She would pay with stale singles all night long.

"I can't just yet," the bartender answered. "Not till

after midnight. The owner thinks we'll turn into drunk pumpkins and ruin his ball. But I'll take a rain check." He smiled, and switched to a bigger rocks glass under the bar, poured Johanna a double shot, and filled her plastic pitcher to the top with no foam.

Johanna guessed he was a Tulane student. She liked his sideburns, hairy scalpels, pointed exacto knives at his temples. Nice wrists. Good watch. Maybe the bartender's rich dad could pay for surgery. "OK," Johanna said. "I'll do that. 12:01, I'm here."

"See you then, if not before," he said, taking her money. "Tips, huh?"

Johanna tried to think fast, as fast as he did. "Don't drink the tap water and don't go past Dauphine late at night by yourself. Yeah, tips. I haven't walked with big bills since tourist season ended." She gulped the double shot and felt the liquor burn. Soon the bourbon would feed the thing, form an alcoholic bubble of a greenhouse. Johanna pushed two extra dollars at the bartender. "Thanks. Keep it. Always happy to pass dirty money along for a job well done. Can I have a glass for my beer?" So he had forgotten a glass; his shirt was starched and his little round glasses looked very fashionable and expensive. Chemo wasn't cheap.

"What's your name?" he asked.

"I can't tell you yet," Johanna said. "I have to go meet other men and decide."

"What?"

"I said I'll tell you later. I have to dance with an old lady I picked up hitchhiking." Johanna danced a two-step, sloshed beer out of the pitcher in one hand, jingled keys and change in her purse with the other.

He laughed and set a plastic cup in front of her.

"Good. I'll watch. Ask for me, David, when you come back if I don't catch you right away, or if you forget what I look like."

"I know. I owe David a bourbon." Johanna picked the cup up with her teeth off the bar top and walked towards the dance floor, searching for an empty front row table.

She was early. Tables were still vacant, but none up front. Johanna settled for one dead center in the bunch. Later she would be surrounded, packed in by normal bodies, looked at, bumped into, asked if she was waiting for anyone else and if she needed all the chairs at her table. She would say yes, unless they wanted to pay for the chairs with shots of bourbon. Or if the inquirers were handsome and all perspiringly male, she would invite them to join her. Johanna set her pitcher and cup on a chair and lifted the side of the table slightly, slid her purse strap with a push of a toe under the leg of the table.

A couple sat down at the table to the left of Johanna's after a while. The woman had neat dyed hair, blonde with black ends. A Sioux stylist must have dipped the tips into a bowl of raven ash and warrior blood. The woman shook her head, ruffled her feather hair. Johanna wanted to fly away, over the Badlands with an eagle's span and feather hair and a down-covered breast and lungs full of clean, cold air.

The man with the bird woman had an accent. Johanna listened. "The Saints are bloody ridiculous. On the two yard line they were, and couldn't get it in. If the coaches had lined up beers in the end zone they mighta done it, but thata been the only way. Bloody terrible, buncha drunks."

Yes, the saints are drunk in New Orleans. You bet your bloody arse they are, my friend, Johanna thought.

The saints don't protect nobody, you bet, let every bloody person get bloody bloody in this town, pal. They grow mold and mildew on their bloody faces, sit by and watch all of us get lumps and die, they do. Johanna laughed into her cup, blew beer up her nose, coughed, thought she would die laughing. They would find her collapsed under the table, the guitarist tripping over her Doc Martin in the aisle during his weaving solo through the crowd. Her arms would be folded in against her breast, frozen in death, featherless wings.

Johanna wiped her face and said to the couple, "Excuse me. I liked your joke. Your hair's great. I'm sorry." They stared as she rose to go to the bathroom. Half her pitcher was gone. She tugged at her purse on the floor, realized, raised the edge of the table, and spilled the remaining half. Beer dribbled to the floor; the plastic pitcher clattered on hardwood. The couple looked concerned and angry: Who was this woman? What was wrong with her? When would her people get there?

In the bathroom mirror, everything was holding up fine. The thing hadn't traveled to the middle of her forehead yet, or to the hollow of her neck, raising itself in a pale green boil. The whites of her eyes weren't yellow with poison. She peed, glad it hadn't moved there, yet.

Poor Jessie the mule, that beast bred for hard work and a good temperament.

His begetting had been backwards, Jessie's father a horse instead of a donkey.

Johanna saw him pull loads of tourists, big bellied men and their big-assed wives, through fumes and car horns, saw him crack his hooves on the paved streets, saw him wait for an imaginary mouse friend to carry a nail file and a tube of fix-it glue into his stall late at

night. He waited and waited for a mending friend.
Finally, he gave up. Jessie was tired of listening about
famous voodoo queens, tired of drinking green water from
the slimy Decatur trough. Tourist babies dropped gooey
ice cream sticks into Jessie's water and foreigners
splashed their hands under his nose, leaving beignet powder hand prints on his flanks. Johanna saw it all; she
didn't blame Jessie one bit. She would run if she were he,
twist her furry head around before she took off, bite
everyone within reach. She would leave big tooth bruises
on fat upper arms, leave reminders of the mule that
didn't mind her master.

Johanna blotted her lipstick on the back of her hand,
on top of the smeared black stamp of Muddy Waters. She
left the bathroom. Her table was taken. Five girls. She
didn't see her pitcher on the floor. Back to David.

"I thought you were supposed to dance with your
friend there," David said to Johanna when she went for
more bourbon.

Johanna turned and looked. An old woman danced by
herself in the middle of the floor to taped music. The band
was setting up its equipment, glancing at the barefooted
woman with their happy eyes, with eyes happy to be in
New Orleans and see New Orleans things, its thing-peo-
ple. "Oh her? No. Mine has pink hair and a blue blouse. I
think mine stood me up. Would you like the hump massage I'd promised to give her if she'd tango with me?"
Johanna rummaged in her purse.

"A, a hump, a hump massage, huh?" David seemed
stuck on the word. "Ah, sure. I'll try anything once."

"Great. I need another round. A bird woman stole my
pitcher and her Saints fan boyfriend took my cup away.
He said I was a bloody something."

David frowned. "Are you sure you want more right now?"

"No. I need more bourbon. I'm feeding."

"Hey, hold on. None for the baby." David was losing the string, the strand of banter, cutting it short between his sideburns.

"I'm not nursing, David. I'm, I'm..." Johanna searched, "I'm feeding my id. No, I mean ego."

"Give it half an hour. The band 'll start in a minute. And I get my break then, when I'll let you buy me that shot."

David wasn't as interesting as Johanna thought. He was a bartender; he should tend to his drinkers. His drinkers gave him crumpled ones for forgetting cups. "Oh fine then," Johanna said. "Half an hour, but, I should tell you, I promised to look up a guy named David."

David looked for something in the wine glasses hanging over his head. "I know him. Who should I say wants him if I see him?"

"Me." Johanna left, couldn't find a spare stool or leftover chair. All gone now.

Johanna found the cigarette machine. Quarters only. She had plenty of those, loose with spare pens and order pads from work at the bottom of her purse, quarters saved for the laundry she didn't do last week. What to smoke? The gold wrapper on the Winstons shone seductively. She plunked her change in, wished a winning lottery ticket would drop down.

The old woman on the dance floor looked out wildly at the crowd from behind her slipping lucite glasses. She shuffled her bare feet, shook the crepey skin around her bare knees. Johanna should go dance with her to give her company. The two of them could request Jessie later and

93

take a starlit gallop through the Quarter. Johanna would daringly jump out when they approached the French Market, run in and steal creole tomatoes. She would catch up and hop back in the buggy, and she and the old dancing lady would eat in the back, dribble tomato juice into their laps, wash down their plunder with swigs from a shared bourbon bottle.

Johanna didn't like to see the woman out there by herself. The dancer seemed to want a partner, a young man to come and sweep her up with an arm around her waist, swing her in fast circles, make her forget that she was old. The eyes behind the glasses wanted that.

Johanna went back to David for matches. He lit her cigarette with a lighter pulled from his pocket. Johanna thought he knew she didn't smoke; he made a funny face. She would take his edge off. "Maybe you could tell me, if he shows up, that is, does David have a girlfriend he's leaving at home in the apartment to come meet me here?"

"No. He used to, but not for a couple months now." David put his hand on the bar and leaned into his shoulder.

He likes this, Johanna thought. She did too. She searched for the outline muscle under his long sleeve. She dragged on her cigarette too hard and coughed again. She'd coughed all night. She knew where the lump had gone. It was eating cilia. Johanna coughed and lost the cigarette from between her fingers at her lips. The cherry of the cigarette dragged across the front of her T-shirt, left a trail of glowing ash across the black cotton covering her breasts. David made a quick motion to brush them off and withdrew his hand just as fast. They would find her crispy on the floor, burned beyond recognition. They would ask David who she was. He would say he didn't know.

Johanna tamped herself out. He was really nice; he was really going to pat her breasts before he checked himself. "My name's Johanna. Nice to meet you, David."

"Nothing like a little fire to bring back the senses, huh?"

How could she explain? "No, nothing like it," Johanna said. She wanted to, wanted to tell him all about the thing, her New Orleans lump. Maybe later. Maybe he would find it and ask about it. She would ask if his family had money.

"Nice to meet you, Johanna." Hillbilly Frankenstein was warming up.

"Yeah, see you in a few," Johanna said and left to sit on a stack of beer cases against the back wall for a better view of the band.

The guitarist was the one to watch. He wore a powder blue tux jacket and pale pink polyester pants. Johanna loved his big Elvis hair and two-toned shoes. He kicked the band into their first song. The drummer smacked his kit; a rocking wisp of a woman plucked a stand-up base. A melon-breasted singer crooned into her mike and flung her hair across her face. A panacea, an intravenous musical drug was what they were. Medicine for the lonely, for the sick, for the mentally faltering, for Johanna. She liked them immediately.

The permanent Christmas lights strung above the bar twinkled. People made nice noises at their tables, chinks of toasting shot glasses, Zippos flaring and clinking shut, good shifting chair and buzzy conversation noises. David would dance with her; people would point behind their own hands at the two of them going to town. The lookers would notice that Johanna didn't wear a bra under her shirt. They would love her. They would love her and make her dance until her hair was wet with sweat, until mascara grayed the crescents below her eyes. She would dance forever for her audience, for David, for, she knew, dead Jessie. She would dance a slow song in memory of him, the free, the crazed, the deranged. Yes, she would run if she were Jessie.

Hillbilly Frankenstein picked up a keyboard player a few songs later. David joined Johanna at her perch during a drum solo. He carried two double shots of bourbon with him. "To dancing when the fat lady sings," he toasted.

"To dancing with the fat lady," Johanna said. She swallowed fast, breathed out, "What's the deal, you don't like to dance? These guys are great."

"Sorry. I dint learn how," he faked in a Cajun drawl, "when I was livin' in hand-me-down blue jean knickers out back in the Bayou. Dint have me no 'special' big sister to teach me."

"You don't need steps to dance to this."

"I'm not into dancing. Love to screw, just not dance."

"My kind of man," Johanna said, rubbing her bicep against the side of her breast. He was as shy as she was. Johanna wanted to take the David puppy home with her and teach him how to sit. She would teach him all kinds of tricks. She would let him find her new nugget with his tongue like he would find the gold crown on the last tooth back by her throat.

David's break was up by the time Johanna found out that he went to the University of New Orleans, graduate something, and that he had green eyes behind the glasses. David walked away with more than that: where she lived, where she worked, her income, her seafood weakness, which of her knees was the trick one. He knew how the small of her back felt through her shirt.

Johanna had meant to make her life up, meant to tell David strange and delicious things about herself. She should have told him about a Paris trip, a halfsister in the FBI, a childhood alien friend, a talking mule in the Quarter named Jessie. What would he do with Johanna and her real life in two days? Why would he want a Jessie?

Johanna couldn't stay. David didn't have her phone number or her last name.

She just wouldn't go back to Muddy Waters anymore. She would wave to David someday from Jessie's back. Johanna and her mule would trot down the street, the yards of her sheer white dress fluttering in the wind. David would turn to look out the window at something and not see the ghost Johanna. He would feel a prickle at the back of his neck, remember a curve of spine he couldn't place. He would pour himself a shot of bourbon and feel the need to dance.

Johanna watched and waited until David was busy with a cluster of customers before sneaking out the door and onto the street. There was a place she had to go to secure a future ride.

A woman in a flowered housecoat stooped to pick up plastic cups and trash in her dirt yard as Johanna walked by on the way to her car. The old woman waved a claw of a hand and smiled at Johanna, showing a big new set of dentures. Johanna waved back, opened her purse, and littered the yard with crumpled dollar bills.

Down Oak, over to St. Charles, around Lee Circle, onto Carondelet, across Canal, back to the Quarter. Johanna knew the way, knew the city, knew the white pillared porches, the palms, the green boulevards, the streetcar tracks, the thick, fat air. She knew where sea level crept above her car tires, above the door handles, above the hood. She knew the sidewalks split open by banana tree trunks, knew the warty streets that cracked as easily as rotten walnuts. She knew the abandoned houses that grew branches out of glassless second story windows, that waved green leaves like eyelashes. She knew her way through the thicket of the city.

The Quarter teemed. Johanna parked in front of a fire hydrant. She left her car unlocked. She walked down Bourbon, turned on Bienville, continued down Exchange Alley to Conti. There she would wait on the broad stone steps of the police building to watch, to listen. She could be a tourist taking a break, resting her feet. If one of the policemen became suspicious, she could go inside for a map and ask directions to Marie Laveau's. Or she could watch for a pretend waiter lover to finish his shift; she could search through all the black and white uniforms that passed, looking for the familiar face, the touch, the arm around her waist. She would wait through the night and into tomorrow, the next day, and the next, wander around in the same striped leggings, dirty her T-shirt with what she wiped off her hands and mouth, use court-yards for toilets and bus stop benches for beds. She would finally return to her stone steps, her lookout. They would find her with a gecko crawling across her cheek, a baby fern sprouting in her hair. They would find New Orleans growing from her body, inside out.

Johanna asked three carriage drivers about Jessie. None knew. After one thirty the crowd on the street became dense, making it harder to see, to hear. She moved to sit on the corner curb and started talking to her lump. "Would you like a beer? Maybe a bit more bourbon. Wasn't that good? Mmm hmm, you liked that, didn't you? It'll be nice and hot tomorrow, and the next day, too." And then the noise broke through. Another chance. Johanna looked around. Traffic was heavy and the driver would have to stop his carriage at the intersection in front of her.

The man clicked his tongue and whistled a quiet sparrow whistle. Johanna stood and approached him. "Excuse me," she said. "Do you know what happened to Jessie today?"

"Jessie?"

"The mule. The one that ran."

"Jess," the driver said in recognition. "He eatin' good tonight, dreamin' sweet dreams of clover. Jess back in his stall and got hisself a two day leave besides. Don't worry, hon. Jess all right. The carriage now – another story." He smiled and clicked his tongue, snapped the reins, and pulled his load of staring people away.

They would find Johanna at the mule trough next week, cooing, her purse stuffed with golden apples and beautiful orange carrots.

Stephen Kimber

As If It Mattered

*T*he *1-0-4?* You. Quizzical. Professorially skeptical. *You mean the 4-0-1.* As if you were lecturing a particularly dense student. Or your wife. As if this kind-eyed cop standing in your front porch telling you your wife has just been killed in a car accident must have gotten her highway route numbers mixed up.

As if the numbers mattered.

The 1-0-4? You mean the 4-0-1. I heard you say it. In my head. In that strapped, trapped-in-place, tumbling, twisting, turmoiled, ice-skidding, gravel-spitting, chassis-flipping, coffees-flying, metal-crunching, airbags-exploding, windshield-shattering, roof-meets-mind, final, strangely never-ending-ever second between what had been and nothingness... I heard you say it.

Even though you hadn't.

Not yet.

But you would.

You did, didn't you?

The 1-0-4? You mean the 4-0-1.

I loved you for it. Perhaps that is why I fell in love

with you. For your uncanny ability to fixate on such an insignificant detail and miss what really matters – to be, so often, so beside the point. I used to think of it – my gender forgive me – as an expression of your endearingly ditzy, feminine side. Or, to give you your male professional due, as a manifestation of your absent-minded professor self.

As you will now have to discover for yourself, I twisted whatever you prefer to call that guileless obtuseness of yours to my own advantage. Not that I intended to.

How could you not have known? You must at least have suspected? How did we end up with our roles so scrambled? I should have been the one listening to the kind-eyed cop. And you should have... Instead of...

The 1-0-4? You mean the 4-0-1.

Of course, I hated you for it too, for your annoying need to be correct. About everything. And anything. Do you remember that time you decided I should take Quinpool Road to get to my office?

"It would be faster," you said.

"No, it wouldn't," I answered. "There's less traffic and fewer lights on Chebucto."

Three weeks later, when I'd forgotten all about the conversation, you brought it up again. "I was right," you said. (You were always right, of course, or perhaps you just never mentioned it again when you were wrong.) As an experiment, you told me, you'd driven each route for a full week during both morning and evening rush hours, then averaged out the times. Taking the Quinpool Road route saved, on average, forty eight seconds' driving time in the mornings, thirty six in the evenings. You. Triumphant.

Did I ever tell you how much I disliked that about

you?

Not that that explains anything. I mean this didn't happen because I hated you for your need to always be right. I did it because... well, that's the question, isn't it?

You mean the 4-0-1.

You were wrong this time. Not that that's your fault. And not that it explains anything either.

I didn't take the flight to Toronto. *Another damn sales meeting,* I'd told you. *Carolyn's panicking about the fall numbers already. So she's called a special meeting. You know how much I hate those meetings. But what can I do? It's just one night.* Me. Resigned.

There was no meeting. No Toronto. And so, no 4-0-1.

I did go to the airport, but only to pick up Hubert. You remember Hubert Durand? The French author? The one whose universities' tour I organized last spring? You don't, do you? Like I said, you always missed what matters. Anyway, let me tell you some other things you don't know that now don't matter anymore either.

Hubert, a professor of literature at some university in Paris, wrote a novel, a truly trashy erotic romance, the translation of which somehow ended up in a discard bin at the *New York Review of Books.* Some reviewer picked it out of the pile, read it, loved it and wrote a review that tarted up Hubert's simple lust story with multiple metaphysical meanings he had never intended nor – believe me when I say this – understood.

His freshly re-interpreted book – repackaged with a gauzy, sepia cover photo that featured mysteriously entwined naked limbs – their naughty bits decorously obscured by breathless blurb copy from the now-infamous review – became a cult phenomenon on North American university campuses (where smut is always welcome, especially when served with a dollop of sanctifying meaning). The publisher, understanding how quickly today's cult success can become tomorrow's pulped returns, immediately decided to cash in with a lecture tour to celebrate the novel's miraculous resurrection from the remainder bin.

Which, of course, is where I came in. You must remember this part. After I'd organized Hubert's east coast stops, the publisher asked if I would accompany him. They were worried his English might not be adequate, that he'd get lost, or disappear, or something. I didn't want to do it. I was trying to nail down the local details of the next Atwood book flog, but the publicity people were insistent. I told you all this at the time; I know I did. Am I telling you again now to try and explain why what happened happened? *I didn't want to go. I didn't intend...*

It's not quite true. While it is fair to say I didn't intend for precisely what happened to happen, I didn't not intend it either – if that make any sense. The only part I really didn't intend was how it has now all ended. I *definitely* didn't intend that.

At any rate, Hubert's English was fine. Better than fine, actually. I met his plane at the airport. By the time we'd rescued his luggage from the carousel, he'd already propositioned me. I won't flatter myself; he was practising his new role as middle-aged campus literary Lothario. He was good at it. And good looking too, in a rumpled, stubbled, smoky, boozy, weathered, French author sort of way that usually doesn't appeal to me.

So why did I say yes? I didn't. In fact, that first time, I laughed at him. Out loud. Perhaps that was because it had been so long since anyone had come on to me like that. You certainly never did. That first night at the bar, I was the one who picked you up. Remember? Five years ago, when my biological clock was still a ticking time bomb. You fit within what I thought at the time were all the requisite father-of my-child parameters: you were male, heterosexual and had a pulse. Better, you were gainfully employed, a tenured professor even, smarter than me, probably kinder. What can I say? I was thirty five; I wasn't thinking straight. Otherwise, I might have asked for a fertility test, or at least a sperm count.

Was that the issue? Too few of your little guys swimming victory laps around my crown jewels? Does that explain everything? Anything? I doubt it. The truth – I never told you this, perhaps because I didn't want to acknowledge it myself – was that your diagnosis was also this condemned woman's minute-before-midnight governor's stay of execution. I was not ready, not fit to be a mother.

As a teenager I remember talking my way out of babysitting jobs – *Test tomorrow... Have to study... So sorry... Why don't you ask my little sister?* – because just the thought of taking care of some crying, clinging, wriggling, shitting, puking helpless little thing scared the hell out of me. In my late twenties, when all my friends suddenly seemed to transform themselves into baby-making factories, I had to force myself to coo and cuddle, and pronounce every Winston-Churchill or rhesus-monkey-looking one of them the most adorable baby I'd ever seen. And, worse, to put up with their mother monsters, my former friends who'd joined the coven, swallowed the Kool-Aid and now professed that having your nipples nibbled raw by an insatiable teething beast was fulfilling, that sleeplessness was its own reward... and, *oh, Chloe, why don't you join us?*

At the time, I thought I must just be jealous. I realize now I was not.

The more we tried – and failed – to conceive, the more I worried we might actually succeed. I can't tell you how relieved I was the day that officious young resident at the clinic finally delivered his male-factor-infertility-for-dummies lecture, complete with personally tailored, colour-coded PowerPoint charts that might have been funny if he – and you – weren't so serious.

See this blue line here, Mrs. Lydon, he explained, a long, elegant finger tracing its trajectory across the computer screen. *This line represents what medical science considers a normal sperm count – twenty million or more sperm per milliliter of semen.* He clicked the mouse and a second, much shorter yellow line magically drew itself beneath the first. *This line shows your count from last week's fertility test, Mr. Lydon. As you can see, it's only eleven million per milliliter, or just over half of the normal level. We call this condition oligospermia, or, in layman's language, low sperm count.* He paused, turned and smiled at both of us. *The good news is that modern artificial reproductive technologies now offer the opportunity for us to assist Mother Nature...*

That was *his* good news, not mine. When I recoiled, the doctors, who quickly became puppy-eager to offer up their cocktails of anti-depressants to deal with my "problem," and assumed my increasingly shrill refusal to consider artificial insemination ("too clinical"), sperm donation ("some pimply-faced guy in a backward baseball cap jerking off into a bottle is not going to be the father my child!"), male fertility drugs ("what if we ended up with some hideous mutant?"), or adoption ("I don't want someone else's damaged goods") was just my understandable, if crazed hormonal response to the news you were not the man you were supposed to be, but that I would get over it, come around, be realistic, adapt.

I didn't. And, when I think about it, you didn't try too hard to change my mind. I wonder now if that was because you were as frightened about having a child as I was. It's too bad we didn't talk more. Perhaps if we had, this would all be easier.

What else can I tell you that will help you make sense of it all now?

The first time? St. John's. Last stop on the tour. After the post-lecture reception at the university. We'd taken a cab back to the hotel.

"A night cap?" he said. "To celebrate such a wonderful evening."

"I should call my husband," I said. And meant it. I was feeling randy from the two glasses of wine and the exhausted exhilaration of having done what I knew was a good job, but all I wanted was to curl up in bed and listen the sound of your voice over the phone.

"Just one?"

"Well... OK... but just one...."

I knew where it was heading, long before the first glass of wine became the second Scotch-on-the-rocks and the third Scotch turned into a coquettish, I-really-shouldn't, sweet-dreams, bottoms-up Bailey's; certainly well before Hubert got off the elevator at my floor instead of continuing on to his own because "a gentleman always sees a lady to her room"; and way before a simple thanks-for-all-your-good-work, goodnight peck on the cheek turned into a gasping, groping dry hump against my hotel room door while Hubert took the plastic room card-lock key from my outstretched hand and slid it into the slot in the door and we tumbled backwards through the opened door onto the carpeted floor, at first giggling and then urgent, rolling, pulling, shrugging, unbuttoning, unzipping...

I'd known where it was heading, and I didn't do anything to stop it. After, I asked myself, *What was I thinking?*, tried to summon up some shame, or, at least, the least regret. I couldn't. I couldn't stop thinking about how good it all felt. Not the sex. The sex itself, as always, was a letdown (if that makes you feel any better). It was the letting go, the giving up, the absolute and total abandonment of all my usual, careful, consider-the-consequences calibrating, measuring, weighing, balancing. The pleasure, the release was in just experiencing the moment. The sex was better than I said (why should I lie now?), but the power of the orgasm had less to do with what was happening between my legs and much more with the absence of what usually happens inside my head.

Even the next morning, I felt remarkably free of guilt, or even angst. Perhaps because I knew the tour was over and I would never have to see Hubert again. Perhaps because I knew you would never find out.

What did I know?

This time – the second time, the time that never actually happened – it was different. Hubert emailed me last week. He'd been invited to speak at some literary conference in Boston and had a few free days afterward. He wrote that he was thinking of flying to Nova Scotia, and wondered if I might be free to show him around and "perhaps renew acquaintances." I wrote back to say – equally blandly – that it was a very busy time for me but that, if he came, "perhaps we could have lunch."

If you're curious, you'll find this exchange of unrevealing correspondence on my computer in a sub-folder of the "Freelance" folder of my email program entitled, "Other…", along with three previous messages from Hubert, including a "Thanks for everything!" message containing a smiley-face emoticon, which he wrote just after he arrived back in Paris the first time, and two even more impersonal messages, including the text of a news story – in French – from a Paris newspaper about his North American tour and a much-forwarded email containing a link to a joke about George Bush eating French fries that I didn't get. Or perhaps wasn't funny. You won't find any other replies from me. There weren't any.

You'll be curious, of course. You'll check my cell phone records – why is it that modern technology makes everything so easy to know and so difficult to understand? – and discover a series of calls to and from Hubert's hotel room in the Boston Marriott, only one of which lasted longer than two minutes. That call, made on a Sunday afternoon three days before he flew to Halifax, was from me to him, went on for twelve minutes and thirty four seconds, and was followed, less than half an hour later, by a one-minute-and twelve-second call from his room to me. And then, three minutes after that, the records will show I placed a call to a number in Sackville, New Brunswick. If you check, you'll find the number is for the Marshlands Inn. You remember that lovely old inn where we stayed on our honeymoon? I'm not very imaginative. If you call, you'll discover I made a reservation for the same room in which we stayed, the one with the sleigh bed and cast iron clawfoot tub. I'm not very inventive either. The reservation is for Mr. and Mrs. Joshua Lydon.

There will be more hints and allegations you'll discover as you go. When the Visa bill comes, for example, you'll notice a purchase from Leeza's Lingerie dated the day after that exchange of phone calls. You'll find the purchase itself – a too lacey, too revealing, much-too-girlish-for-me pink peignoir set – in my suitcase with the price tag still on. You won't know this – except that I'm telling you – but I left the tag attached in case I chickened out and decided to return it instead. (Leeza's has a strict thirty-day returns policy, so you shouldn't wait too long...) My God, such strange advice I'm offering you! Think of it as the practical side of my personality, showing itself even in death. I mean, there's no point for you to keep it... unless... do you have secrets too?

How little we really know about anyone.

And even what we think we know... do we really know it at all?

I would like to tell you I planned to call it off – whatever this "it" really was. I did. In fact, in the days of doubt between that flurry of Sunday phone calls and the arrival of Flight AC8894 at 10:38 on Wednesday morning, I considered calling Hubert to cancel many times. The cell phone logs don't count calls considered but not made.

I would like to tell you I was hesitant because I loved you. But then I would have to tell you that I went ahead anyway because I didn't love you. And neither is quite true.

If you must know, you had very little to do with either decision. Neither did Hubert. It was, as so many things are, mostly just about me. About the positive job evaluation I got. And the raise I didn't. About the fact I actually cared about either. About the jeans that no longer fit the way I'd imagined they once did. About my father's cancer. And my mother's loneliness. About the new computer program I can't seem to make do what the ads claimed it would. About the hot flashes that began before I was ready for them. About all the people I never became. And the one I did. About me.

It was as twisted and as uncomplicated as that. Escape from reality. Pretend for a day and a night. And then back to my life, my job, my husband.

No one would ever know.

So much for that.

It was different than the first time. We – I – couldn't pretend I didn't know the road we were traveling down. Literally. Figuratively. We stopped for coffee in Truro. Hubert had acquired a taste for Tims double-doubles during his last visit. We talked about the success of his book and his inability to write the next one, the conference in Boston and the pretentiousness of academics, the war in Iraq, the first signs of spring in Boston and the far-from-last vestiges of winter in Nova Scotia, the unlikely prospect that a Nova Scotia vintner could ever produce a wine Hubert would consider acceptable ... everything, that is, except the fact this was all a huge mistake, and that it shouldn't have happened the first time, and that it couldn't happen again.

I was saving that conversation for after dinner. No, later. For after sex. Or, perhaps, later still, for those few minutes tomorrow in the airport lounge after he'd checked in for his flight back to Boston and before he proceeded through Security. *It's been fun, Hubert*, I was going to tell him, *and good for me in a strange kind of way* – it's important to be honest – *but it can't go on. I have a husband. And a job. And a life. Goodbye...*

Do you believe that? Do *I* believe that?

Not that it matters now, of course. We never made it

to the inn, let alone to dinner, sex, breakfast, back to the airport. We never had the conversation.

It was early afternoon. Around two, I'm guessing. The sky – grey, gloomy, heavy with menace and malice – pressed down hard against the frozen landscape while wind-whipped snow squalls chased each other angrily across the road in the beams of the car's headlights. We were driving along the 1-0-4 somewhere between Wentworth and Oxford. I used to know all the landmarks but, ever since they replaced the old, winding, "too dangerous" road with a new toll highway a few years ago, it all looks the same to me.

I needed a cigarette. I know, I know. I don't smoke, and haven't since long before I met you. But I had one that first night in St. John's. After. Hubert was still on his back, waiting for his breathing to slow down. I was tucked into the crook of his arm, feeling the room spin. He reached over to his sports jacket and pulled a pack of Gitanes from its inside pocket, lit one, and held it out to me. I arched my neck up toward his proffered hand, took a long, slow drag and remembered how much I used to like the sensation of smoking. Do you remember me joking that if the doctor ever told me I had a terminal illness, the first thing I'd do was go out and buy a package of cigarettes – or was that from before I met you? Not that it matters. Smoking kills. Trust me on that.

Hubert had left his package of cigarettes in the well between the car's front seats, along with my sunglasses and cellphone, and his new iPod. You would have been proud of me. I know how much you hate when I get distracted putting on my makeup while driving. I didn't look down, just kept my eyes fixed on the snowy nothingness in front of me and felt around with my right hand like a

111

blind man until I felt the familiar shape of the cardboard packaging.

"Want one?" I asked Hubert.

"Sure," he said. "But, please, let me..."

"No, no, that's OK. I can do it." I had a sudden image – black and white, from a fifties' movie, a romantic comedy, perhaps? – of me with two unlit cigarettes dangling from my mouth, lighting one, passing it across to Hubert and then lighting my own.

Smooth.

Not so much in real life.

I did manage to get both cigarettes out of the package, insert them, filters facing correctly, into my mouth and, then, more awkwardly than in the picture in my mind's eye, lit each of them with the car's lighter. But, as I reached back up to take the first from my mouth and hand it to Hubert, I somehow knocked the second from between my lips. It fell into my lap. Instinctively, I looked down and frantically began to use my right hand to brush it off my slacks. Wrong hand. Now, one burning cigarette had fallen onto the seat between my legs, the other had become – thanks to me – a shower of sparks burning pinprick holes in my slacks. Had I packed another pair? I–

"Merde! Non–"

I looked up, saw the red tail lights of a monster eighteen-wheeler looming up out of the snow swirls dead ahead of us. We were going too fast; it wasn't going fast enough. We were about to rear-end a transport truck!

"No! Fuck–"

I slammed on the brakes and, at the same time, twisted the steering wheel to my left, thinking, 'If I can just get past him, everything will be OK.' But then it wasn't. An air horn blast just above and behind me! Oh, no.

There was a second truck. In the outside lane. Trying to pass me and the first truck. Sandwich time. I dragged the steering wheel back to my right, felt the hurricane whoosh of the second truck as it barreled past to my left. Breathed again. Braking had put some distance between me and the truck in front. It was going to be OK. I almost had time to feel the pain from the cigarette still burning between my legs. Almost. The car's rear end fishtailed as it hit a patch of black ice. Was this a metaphor for my life? Just when you think... Brake? Don't brake? Brake. Jolt. Gravel. Pavement. Ice. Gravel again. Then flying. And then silence.

And then everything happened at once, and didn't happen at all.

Which was when I heard you say it.

The 1-0-4? You mean the 4-0-1.

I wanted to explain, make you understand that this wasn't about Hubert, or you, or us; that it was about me; that none of the explanations explained anything because there was no explaining anything; that I was sorry for what you could never know; that I'd loved you in my way, been true to you in my fashion.

As if any of it mattered.

But I couldn't.

I'm dead.

Anne Stockwell

The Truth of the Truism

Count your blessings. Make a gratitude list. Walk a mile in the other guy's shoes. One day you'll understand.

When I was 12, sentiments like that cropped up all the time in the lectures I got from exasperated adults. The issue was my attitude. I didn't want anything I had, and I often made that plain. I could not be comforted, reached out to, or reasoned with.

My world had literally frozen. With my parents newly divorced, I had been sent away to Minnesota to live with relatives who soon registered their ambivalence about me. Where walking to school in Louisiana had taken me past live oaks and bait shops, the same twice-daily trek in Minneapolis was all about getting a running start up that icy hill that waited to send me and my book sack tumbling back into the mud. My face instantly bloomed in acne, accompanied by doomed and various sexual yearnings. Socially the best I could do was chess club. I was so lonely I had no tears.

It was an unwary adult who took me aside for a pep talk. I already had the gift of a sharp tongue, and I saved my worst for people who tried to make me feel better. How can I convey the rage I felt, realizing that my adolescent troubles were perfectly visible even to people I didn't respect or admire? It was outrageous to find myself so oversimplified. On the outside, I knew, I was just a sullen 12-year-old. But inside I felt the full breadth of my soul, and I was at odds with the world.

Obviously I was too insignificant to inflict harm on my opponent. So I framed the conflict as a siege. I wouldn't participate in what I disagreed with. By not opting in, I would hold out. In particular, I hated those little sayings meant to soften reality. In my view adults who said things like "count your blessings" had simply lost the moral energy to face facts.

For the record, I don't know why nobody slapped me silly. I'm now comfortable with the understanding that this is just one of a million things I don't know – and never will.

As I write this, I'm older than any of those adults who took me aside back then. More years have passed than I could have imagined. I've become one of those people who thinks it's reasonable to count their blessings. How did I get here from there? Through grownup loss, which clarified everything.

When I first fell in love, and my love was returned, I felt such joy that my capacity for happiness doubled. The feeling actually created the space that received it.

Later I lost that love and was flooded with pain. But when the pain subsided, my new capacity for happiness didn't. That space in me was meant to be joyful, and soon enough, it was. The big adult losses made me stronger, just as the old clichés promised.

A few years ago, I was told that I had a life-threatening illness. Here's what happened. In the silence just after the doctor said the bad word, my life passed before my eyes. It really did. There's no other way to say it.

In that instant, I completely understood that my life was beautiful. I felt a rush of gratitude so powerful, my body vibrated. It was as though somebody had plugged me in and now I was lit. Every day since, I've felt that same current. Every sight, sound, sensation has been heightened. Every laugh is louder, every smell sharper.

Life, for me, turns out to be a code I'm deciphering a little at a time. Those old chestnuts – "count your blessings" and the rest – turn out to be overflowing with meaning. They're empty only when you're too green to fill them. When I meet young people now who are too sarcastic to be touched, I know they're hurt. When someone tells me love is phony, I know someone else has disappointed him. When people talk about dying...well, I still fear dying. But one day I'll understand that too, and then I won't be afraid.

For today, life goes on, and every minute is precious to me. I don't count my blessings. They are countless.

Anita Hanson

Creative Non-function

Dear Barb,

Sorry it's been so long since I've written. I lost my address book a while ago, and couldn't write to anyone until I remembered that I'd saved last year's Christmas cards and they had a lot of the return addresses on them, but I couldn't remember where I'd put them, and then when I finally found the cards I kept forgetting to buy a new little book to write the addresses in, but then I realized they didn't really need to be in a book before I could use them, so now I can finally write to you again.

And I have the most amazing news! Do you remember way back in high school how you guys used to tease me about being a space cadet sometimes? Like that time I stayed up almost all night studying for a math exam, but the exam was in physics? Or the time my Mom let me take her car to school, but then I forgot and took the bus home and left her car sitting in the parking lot? Sometimes it was kind of funny but usually it wasn't, and it would make me feel just awful. Like the time that horrible teacher we had for Biology – what was it we called him? It was something like Yogi or Smokey or something like that. I know it always made me think of a bear. Anyhow, one time he caught me staring out the window when we were supposed to be doing the drawing of the frog and he made me stand up and right in front of everybody he said I was the perfect example of a person with lots of potential who was never going to succeed at anything because I would never apply myself and I was so mortified I just wanted to cry.

Mr. Pooh! That's what we called him! His real name was Mr. Pulanski.

Anyhow, back to my news. What happened was, my friend Anne – do you remember Anne? She was the one who stopped speaking to me that time when I drove her to the airport, but I was a half hour late picking her up and the traffic was bad so she missed her plane. She was going to the Dominican with her friend Karen and Karen made it on time and ended up in the Dominican all by herself and was really mad. Or was it the Bahamas? I forget. But then she started speaking to me again and said I was an okay friend as long as we didn't do anything time-sensitive. Anyhow, Anne showed me a magazine that had an article in it that she said made her think of me, and I thought she was right, so I went to some doctors and got checked out and guess what – it turns out I have Attention Deficit Disorder! I don't know if Karen is still mad at Anne, that was a while ago.

I thought it was only kids who had it, but they told me it doesn't really go away when you grow up, it's just that you kind of get used to it and learn how to get by even though your thoughts keep jumping around, but it makes a lot of things harder, because it makes you forgetful and disorganized and absent-minded.

When I tell everyone that I have it, sometimes they don't believe me and sometimes they say that there's no such thing, that it's just another excuse – like Wanda. I went for lunch with her a while ago and I had a Greek salad wrap (That's my new favourite thing – I just lo-o-o-ove Greek salad wraps. Do you ever order them? Seems like they wouldn't be all that hard to make, I should try to make one myself sometime), and that's what she said, that there's no such thing. She said her little niece Julie is smart but never listens in class and never finishes her homework and is always late for school and her parents say it's not her fault because she's ADD, but Wanda says really she's just spoiled and lazy and irresponsible and would do fine if she'd only try harder. Julie's the cutest little thing, with huge big brown eyes and curly hair. I met her once when Wanda was babysitting her for her sister. Or is it her brother? Doesn't matter. So Wanda says it's the same for me. And even some doctors say there's no such thing, so sometimes I'm just not sure what's true and what isn't. I think Julie is eight.

When I told Gary, he didn't seem too bothered. He said after 22 years (Yes! we've been married 22 years – can you believe it? Do you still have the bridesmaid dress you wore for our wedding? Those were the ugliest dresses. I don't know why I ever picked them), he was used to me, and that he likes me the way I am. He says he doesn't mind always getting stuck doing all the planning and organizing and my doctor says I'm really lucky to have such a patient guy, that a lot of them get super frustrated and can't take it anymore and end up divorced. Did you hear that Lorraine and Ron got divorced? I must get a card off to poor Lorraine. That was almost two years ago and I still haven't written to her.

In fact, most of the time I think I mind more than he does. He always has to remind me about things, and has to wait for me to finish getting ready every time when we're going out, and quick has to tidy up whenever company comes over because I always leave everything in such a mess. Sometimes I just feel like I'm totally useless and will never be able to do anything right. I think maybe that's why I get depressed every once in a while.

At least now I know why I always act this way, but it's still frustrating, because that doesn't change it. I <u>still</u> miss the exit every time I go to Costco. Are you a member at Costco? They had some really good grapes there last week. And I <u>still</u> need a note on the kitchen counter every week to remind me that Friday is garbage day, even though Friday has been garbage day for twenty years. They even pick up on Good Friday – that really surprised me.

So what's new with you?

Love,
Margie

Erika Ritter

Found on the Subway

FOREWORD

Hello there. So you found my notebook. Where was it
– just left on a bench in the subway station? (That would
be so me.) Or maybe fluttering forlornly on some sewer
grate, after it fell out of my satchel. (Again, how typically
careless.) Note that I'm giving you the benefit of the
doubt in assuming it was found-- you know, as opposed to
dog-robbed off my corpse in some desolate alley?

But hey, however you came by it, chances are, you're
curious about the contents. At least curious enough to
benefit from a brief introduction to help you decide
whether it's worth your while to read any further.

Looking for thrills, spills and non-stop action? If so,
take my advice and leave this book where you found it,
for somebody else. What follows are mere notes from the
underground. One person's quotidian observations while
in motion. Likely, you've logged sufficient hours yourself
on the subway to know that excitement is seldom the
watchword down here.

On the other hand, this is our milieu. This is where we find ourselves, day in and day out. Why shouldn't we at least try to derive meaning from the place where so much of our waking (and okay, sometimes sleeping) lives are passed? Why not do our very best to eke as much universe as we can from this particular subterranean snowflake?

Anyway, such was my reasoning, when I bought this book and set myself the task of preserving public transit life. You see, more and more lately, my friend, (if I may presume to call you my friend, regardless of how this notebook came into your possession) I have been assailed by feelings of – well, what? Weariness, shall we say. Along with a certain staleness. Not to speak of growing concern about all the flat and unprofitable uses of this world.

All right, so you recognize that reference. Why not? You took Hamlet in high school, just like everybody else. For all I know, you got five-out-of-five on the final exam for correctly identifying the play, the speaker of the quotation, the scene number, the context, and the consequences. But please understand I'm plagiarizing to make a point. After all, deciding to jot down in his "tables" observations about the world around him later helps kick-start Hamlet out of his ennui. So maybe anyone can benefit from keeping a running tab on the passing scene.

And these days, what scene could be more multifarious than the subway, with its cross-section of ages, races, genders, and economic classes? Okay, you won't see a lot of rich, white, middle-age guys strap-hanging along with the hoi-polloi. But otherwise, what's on the carte du jour here is your basic Microcosm o' Humanity-In-a-Basket.

That said, be forewarned that there are limits to what

I (and therefore you) can expect to learn about life through my observations underground. I (and therefore you) will have to take folks more or less as I find them, and I can't guarantee either the freshness of my insights, or the depth of my analyses. In other words, no verities on offer, all right?

Much less eternal verities. Even as I write these words — heck, maybe even as you read them — time and the train have both moved on. What I've written about is already past — and passed — along with the fact of your reading what I've recorded, including the fact that I'm recording it. (Whew!)

However, by way of small consolation to us both: Once you and I turn this page, what I wrote will still be there, indelibly pressed between two covers, irrespective of whether you or I or anyone else ever glances at it again. Kind of a Taoist thing, if you look at it like that.

Or, a crackpot thing, depending on your point of view. Hey, you're the one who found the notebook I lost. Go ahead and look at it any way you want.

* * *

Standing on the subway platform, where this patient West Indian nanny is trying to coax a very self-assured white kid, maybe four years old, into eating his snack. "Come on, now," she tells him. "Yesterday, I give you cream cheese and crackers and you don't want it. Today I make you peanut butter and crackers and you don't like that either."

But the little kid still won't eat, and for some reason, the nanny catches my eye, and sighs. So I remark to the kid: "You're a tough customer."

At this, the little boy squares his shoulders and fixes me with a look of upper-class scorn. "I am not a 'customer'!" he informs me coldly.

(Conclusion drawn: Do not speak to children of privilege unless spoken to.)

* * *

What is going on here? Only three stops along the line, and this car is already loaded down with people loaded down like bellhops. We're talking major luggage here: bulky shoulder bags bristling with purpose-built pockets full of everything from cell phones, to Day-Timers, to toothbrushes, to I-Pods, to knitting needles, to the complete Encyclopedia Britannica on CD ROM, and more.

There are teenage girls with the inevitable stuffed koalas and My Little Ponies dangling from their bloated backpacks. And, oops, here comes a burly man hauling a huge canvas duffle-bag, suitable for transporting dismembered bodies home from the hockey arena.

Like bumper stickers, only much less portable, all this paraphernalia proclaims who these people are and what they're about, to a car full of strangers. Meanwhile, all I've got on me is my small satchel with a few subway tokens, plus this notebook. Uh-oh. What if there's some disaster lurking down the line everybody but me knows about, and I'm the only one who left home without a complete Identi-Kit to help out the folks from Forensics?

Now here's a guy who's come prepared for all contingencies, including bivouac in the Hindu Kush. How else to explain his big metal-framed rucksack, bashing everyone in the aisle every time he turns? What all has he got in there — a bedroll, groundsheet, collapsible cutlery, maybe even a pup-tent? Just in case — I don't know — the dental appointment he's heading for runs long? Or maybe, before he gets there, some electrical emergency will halt the train, and make it necessary for him to pitch his tent and make camp, right here in our aisle. He can only hope.

* * *

Overheard on the subway car — Man in suit to other man in suit: So, how's your busy-ness quotient these days?
Other man in suit: Oh, about the same.
(Conclusion drawn: Hunh?)

* * *

The subway driver attempts to amuse himself and us by broadcasting the stops in various voices, from The Godfather, to John Lennon, to — inevitably — Rod Serling. In response, he draws a few wan smiles from those grateful for random acts of creativity. Others, however, are shaking their heads. Is it in sympathy for the all-too-apparent boredom of his job? Or — annoyance at attention being called to the repetitive tedium of all our lives?

* * *

On an outdoor platform — The guy beside me is taking advantage of being above ground to check and re-check his cell phone for new messages. I know that's what he's doing because, between checks and re-checks, he punches various numbers and then asks the person who answers: "Did you just try to call me?" So far, it seems nobody did. Yet he can't seem to devote himself simply to waiting for the train.

Recently, I read about something called CPA – Continuous Partial Attention. Apparently it's an affliction among people who have to be plugged in by phone or email all the time, even while they're doing something else. Frankly, I'd think better of his calls if he was making them from a payphone. Someone seen through Plexiglas always appears to be miming a conversation that looks genuinely urgent. A cry for help, a plea for understanding, a groan of existential angst. Like that painting I once saw. Edward Hopper, maybe? (Note to self: Check out American Art book from library again.) An anonymous, lone figure inside a phone booth, beside a gas station on the edge of a highway, connected by one thin, tenuous wire to the unseen universe.

So much for the quiet, bygone drama of phone booths. Right here we got Cell-Phone Guy, announcing loudly to whoever's captive on the other end: "Gotta go. Train's here." Of course, he's not talking to me. That's the worst of cell-phoners, the way they take over public space as if it belongs to them, and force the rest of us to eavesdrop. Bring back pay phones, I say, and – Oops! Train is here. In my universe as well as his.

* * *

God, this is amazing. No, I mean it really is. Don't look now, but God just sat down in the seat beside me. And He wants to chat. Is it rude of me to keep on writing? I don't want to miss getting this down, but on the other hand, maybe God would prefer to keep our conversation strictly off the record?

Luckily, God – being God – sees right to the heart of my problem. Don't worry, He tells me, Take all the notes you want. I assume you must be a journalist.

No, no, nothing like that, I tell God. I wouldn't even know what to ask.

You mean you've never interviewed an international celebrity before? God joshes.

Just once, I tell Him. A guy in a bar who said he was Napoleon. But he turned out to be surprisingly uninteresting.

Well, if you're not in the media, says God, what's with the notebook?

So, it seems there are limits to His omniscience. I explain I'm trying to find some meaning to life here on the subway.

Let me take a look, God says. But He frowns as He reads over some of my entries. My handwriting, maybe?

Well, you've got an eye for detail, is His comment as He hands back my book. Yet there's a tone of criticism I'm not so crazy about.

Of course. He thinks I'm knocking His handiwork. I'm sorry, I tell Him. This is just how the chips fell.

Excuse Me? says God. An entire day on the subway, and not one observation of something uplifting, satisfying, or remotely meaningful about the human condition?

Don't You think I'd have preferred something a little more transcendent? I ask. But I can only work with the materials at hand, and...

Poppycock! God says.

Really, He said that. Of course, God's got that Lord-thundering-Jehovah thing happening, and "Poppycock!"

127

never sounded so magisterial.

You want meaningful? Uplifting? Transcendent, even? God booms so loudly, even folks muffled under headphones are looking over at Him in surprise.

With His forefinger – in a gesture I recognize from that painting on the Sistine ceiling by the artist I can never remember (note to self: Check out Art of the Renaissance book from library again) – God points to a dad in a corner of the subway car, paging through a picture-book alongside a small, rapt child, who presses her tiny, running-shoed feet together, sole to sole, like praying hands.

I saw that, I fib to God. I was on the verge of writing it down.

But God is caught up in the moment, and pays no attention. There's your universe in a snowflake, He proclaims, still pointing. Or, what about that old man reaching out, oh so tenderly, to close the jaw of his slumbering wife? Or that teenage boy with a mouthful of braces, very aw-shucks, as he offers his seat to the woman juggling twins?

All right, all right, I concede, scribbling as fast as I can. It's very heartwarming. Yet, does it make Your subway-as-microcosm so much more legitimate than mine? I mean, what if that kind father suddenly slaps his little girl's feet off the seat? Or – God forbid – that sweet old man deliberately jostles You with a sharp elbow on his way off the train ? Or the boy with the braces blares in Your ear: "So, I like fucking go, 'Go fuck yourself.'" What then? Would any of them be disqualified as a meaningful representative of humanity?

No, of course not, God says. No more than you're disqualified, for overlooking the heartwarming stuff right under your nose. It's a big tent, is all I'm saying, God continues. I designed it that way on purpose. Though, not such a big tent that it can't be schlepped in a backpack onto the subway.

Wow! Great stuff! I tell God, as I write furiously. Not that I necessarily agree with You, but this has to be the most interesting conversation I've ever had, with anyone.

Sure, says God. Look at the competition: Some nut-job in a bar who thinks he's Napoleon.

Wait a minute, I say. You mean that wasn't Napoleon?

Har-dee-har, says God, You're a regular wiseacre.

Whatever that is. (Note to self: look up "wiseacre" in Dictionary of Antiquated Slang.)

All of a sudden, God looks around sharply and leaps up. Whoops, He says, This is My stop!

Aren't they all Your stops? I ask Him.

No answer. God is gone. Not that I – oh, okay, what the heck. By now, gentle reader, you're onto me. You've guessed that wasn't God sitting beside me on the subway, any more than the guy in the bar that time was Napoleon.

So why would I try to con you, of all people? After all, you're the person who found my notebook, right? You've been patient enough to slog through it, up to this point. (At least, I'm assuming you have.)

Well – I just figure by now you're entitled to an inspirational interlude, as much as I am. I only hope you weren't tempted to skip through the part with God in it. Because even if God is just a device of mine, I think you'll agree He's the best thing so far in the book. It's His attitude, am I right? Not to speak of that resonant delivery.

The point being, my outlook's been changed for the

better by that brief epiphany. Now, I feel that I could ride the subway all the way to the end of the line and back again, over and over, and end up with inoperable writer's cramp, without ever scratching the surface of the veritable cavalcade of ordinary wonders available

Does any of what goes on down here – or up there, for that matter – truly mean anything? Who can say? All I know is that it definitely makes me feel better, to have captured some of it between these two covers. Whether you'll feel better for having read what I've written so far is another question.

And not my problem. Hey, as far as I'm concerned, I've done my part, by losing this notebook. Just for the opportunity to share with a stranger what I found on the subway.

Jane Urquhart

Storm Glass

(This story first appeared in the book "Storm Glass", published by McClelland & Stewart; used by permission of Jane Urquhart and McClelland & Stewart.)

From where she lay she could see the lake. It seemed to her to be heading east, as if it had a definite destination in mind and would someday be gone altogether from the place where it was now. But it was going nowhere; though diminished by sun, replenished by rain and pushed around by strong winds, it was always a lake. And always there. God knows it had its twentieth-century problems; its illnesses, its weaknesses. Some had even said it was dying. But she knew better. She was dying, and although she felt as close as a cousin to the lake, she did not sense that it shared with her this strong, this irreversible decline. It would always be a lake, and always there, long after she had gone somewhere else. Alone.

She was alone in the room now. As alone as she would be a few months later where the brightness of the last breath closed on the dark, forever. She had imagined the voyage in that dark – her thoughts speaking in an

131

alien tongue – textural black landscape – non-visual – swimming towards the change. And then she had hoped she would be blessed with some profound last words, some small amount of theatre to verify the end of things. But somehow she sensed it would be more of a letting go, slipping right through the centre of the concentric circles that are the world and into a private and inarticulate focus, and then...

The shore had changed again and again since her first summers there. One year there had been unexpected sand for her babies to play in. She remembered fine grains clinging to their soggy diapers, and their flat sturdy footprints which had existed for seconds only before the lake gathered them up. But a storm the following winter had altered the patterns of the water and the next year her small children had staggered over beach stones to the edge. In subsequent weeks their bare feet had toughened, allowing them to run over rocks and pebbles without pain. Her own feet had resisted the beach stones summer after summer, forcing her to wear some kind of shoes until she left the land for the smooth softness of the water.

Her husband, larger, more stubborn, less willing to admit to weaknesses than she, would brave the distance of the beach, like the children, barefoot. But his feet had never toughened, and standing, as she sometimes had, on the screened veranda, she had watched the pain move through his stiffened legs and up his back until, like a large performing animal, he had fallen, backwards and laughing, into the lake.

He was not there now, unwilling to admit to this, her last, most impossible weakness.

Yet he came and went, mostly at mealtimes, when a

hired woman came to cook for them. He came in heavy with the smell of the farm where he had worked and worked, making things come to be; a field of corn, a litter of pigs, or even a basket of smooth, brown eggs. The farm took all of his time now, as if, as she moved down this isolated tunnel towards that change, it was even more important that he make things come to be. And though this small summer cottage was only minutes away from the earth that he worked, the fact of her lying there had made it a distance too great for him to travel except for the uncontrollable and predictable necessities of hunger and of sleep.

The beach was smaller this year, and higher. Strong spring winds had urged the lake to push the stones into several banks, like large steps, up to the grass. These elevations curved in a regular way around the shoreline as if a natural amphitheatre had been mysteriously provided so that audiences of pilgrims might come and sit and watch the miracle of the lake. They never arrived, of course, but she sometimes found it fun to conjure the image of the beach filled with spectators, row on row, cheering on the glide of a wave, the leap of a fish, the flash of a white sail on the horizon. In her imagination she could see their backs, an array of colourful shirts, covering the usual solid grey of the stones.

And yet, even without the imaginary spectators, the grey was not entirely solid. Here and there a white stone shone amongst the others, the result of some pre-Cambrian magic. In other years the children had collected these and old honey pails full of them still lined the windowsills on the porch. The children had changed, had left, had disappeared into adulthood, lost to cities and success. And yet they too came and went with smiles and

133

gifts and offers of obscure and indefinite forms of help. She remembered mending things for them; a toy, a scratch on the skin, a piece of clothing, and she understood their helpless, inarticulate desire to pretend that now they could somehow mend her.

In her room there were two windows. One faced the lake, the other the weather, which always seemed to come in from the east. In the mornings when the sun shone, a golden rectangle appeared like an extra blanket placed on the bed by some anonymous benevolent hand. On those days her eyes moved from the small flame of her opal ring to the millions of diamonds scattered on the lake and she wished that she could lie out there among them, rolling slightly with the current until the sun moved to the other side of the sky. During the heat of all those summers she had never strayed far from the water, teaching her children to swim or swimming herself in long graceful strokes, covering the distance from one point of land to another, until she knew by heart the shoreline and the horizon visible from the small bay where the cottage was situated. And many times she had laughed and called until at last, with a certain reluctance, her husband had stumbled over the stones to join her.

He seldom swam now, and if he did it was early in the morning before she was awake. Perhaps he did not wish to illustrate to her his mobility, and her lack of it. Or perhaps, growing older, he wished his battle with the lake to be entirely private. In other times she had laughed at him for his method of attacking the lake, back bent, shoulders drawn forward, like a determined prize fighter, while she slipped effortlessly by, as fluid as the water, and as relaxed. His moments in the lake were tense, and quickly finished; a kind of enforced pleasure, containing more comedy than surrender.

But sometimes lately she had awakened to see him, shivering and bent, scrambling into his overalls in some far corner of the room and knowing he had been swimming, she would ask the customary questions about the lake. "Was it cold? Was there much of an undertow?" and he had replied with the customary answers. "Not bad, not really, once you are in, once you are used to it."

That morning he had left her early, without swimming. The woman had made her bed, bathed her and abandoned her to the warm wind that drifted in one window and the vision of the beach and the lake that occupied the other. Her eyes scanned the stones beyond the glass trying to remember the objects that, in the past, she had found among them. Trying to remember, for instance, the look and then the texture of the clean dry bones of seagulls; more delicate than the dried stems of chrysanthemums and more pleasing to her than that flower in full bloom. These precise working parts of once animate things were so whole in themselves that they left no evidence of the final breakdown of flesh and feather. They were suspended somewhere between being and non-being like the documentation of an important event and their presence somehow justified the absence of all that had gone before.

But then, instead of bone, she caught sight of a minuscule edge of colour, blue-green, a dusty shine, an irregular shape surrounded by rounded rocks – so small she ought not to have seen it, she ought to have overlooked it altogether.

"Storm glass," she whispered to herself, and then she laughed realizing she had made use of her husband's words without thinking, without allowing the pause of reason to interrupt her response as it so often did. When they spoke together she sometimes tried expressly to avoid his words, to be in possession of her own, hard thoughts. Those words and thoughts, she believed, were entirely her own. They were among the few things he had no ability to control with either his force or his tenderness.

In must have been at least fifteen summers before, when the children, bored and sullen in the clutches of earlier adolescence, had sat day by day like ominous boulders on the beach, until she, remembering the honey pails on the windowsills, had suggested that they collect the small pieces of worn glass that were sometimes scattered throughout the stones. Perhaps, she had remarked, they could do something with them; build a small patio or path, or fill glass mason jars to decorate their bedrooms. It would be better, at least, than sitting at the water's edge wondering what to do with the endless summer days that stretched before them.

The three children had begun their search almost immediately; their thin backs brown and shining in the hot sun. Most of the pieces they found were a dark ochre colour, beer bottles no doubt, thrown into the lake by campers from the provincial park fifteen miles down the road. But occasionally they would come across a rarer commodity, a kind of soft turquoise glass similar to the colour of bottles they had seen in antique shops with their mother. These fragments sometimes caused disputes over who had spotted them first but, as often as not, there were enough pieces to go fairly around. Still rarer and smaller were the particles of emerald green and navy blue, to be found among the tiny damp pebbles at the very edge of the shore, the remnants of bottles even more advanced in age than those that were available in the shops. But the children had seen these intact as well, locked behind the glass of display cases in the county museum. Often the word *poison* or a skull and crossbones would be visible in raised relief across the surface of this older, darker glassware. Their mother knew that the bottles had held cleaning fluid, which was as toxic now in its cheerful tin and plastic containers as it had been then housed in dark glass, but the children associated it with dire and passionate plots, perhaps involving pirates, and they held it up to their parents as the most important prize of all.

The combing of the beach had lasted two days, maybe three, and had become, for a while, the topic of family conversations. But one evening, she remembered, when they were all seated at the table, her husband had argued with her, insisting as he often did on his own personal form of definition – even in the realm of the activities of children.

"It's really storm glass," he had announced to the children who had been calling it by a variety of different names, "that's what I always called it."

"But," she had responded, "I remember a storm glass from high school, from physics, something to do with predicting weather, I don't know just what. But that's what it is, not the glass out there on the beach."

"No," he had continued, "storms make it with waves and stones. That wears down the edges. You can't take the edge of a piece of glass that lies at the bottom of a bird bath. Storms make it, it's storm glass."

"Well, we always called it beach glass, or sometimes water glass when we were children, and the storm glass came later when we were in high school."

"It is storm glass," he said, with the kind of grave finality she had come to know; a statement you don't retract, a place you don't return from.

It was after these small, really insignificant, disputes that they would turn silently away from each other for a while; she holding fiercely, quietly, to her own privacy, her own person. To him it seemed she refused out of stubbornness to accept his simplified sense of the order of things, that she wished to confuse him by leaning towards the complexities of alternatives. He was not a man of great intellect. Almost every issue that he had questioned had settled into fact and belief in early manhood. He clung to the predictability of these preordained facts with such tenacity that when she became ill the very enormity of the impending disorder frightened him beyond words and into the privacy of his own belief that it was not so, could not be happening to her, or, perhaps more importantly, to him. They did not speak of it but turned instead quietly from each other, she not wishing to defend her own tragedy, and he not wishing to submit to any reference to such monumental change.

But fifteen years before, in the small matter of the glass, the children had submitted easily, as children will, to the sound of his authority; and storm glass it had become. Within a week, however, their project had been abandoned in favour of boredom and neither path nor patio had appeared. Nevertheless, the glass itself appeared year after year among the stones on the beach and, try as she might, she could never quite control the impulse to pick it up. The desire to collect it was with her even now, creating an invisible tension, like a slim, taught wire, from her eyes to her hands to the beach as she lay confined within her room. It was, after all, a small treasure, an enigma; broken glass robbed by time of one of its more important qualities, the ability to cut. And though she could no longer rub it between her palms she knew it would be as firm and as strong as ever. And as gentle.

From where she lay she could see the lake and she knew that this was good; to be able to see the land and the end of the land, to be able to see the vast indefinite bowl of the lake. And she was pleased that she had seen the storm glass. She felt she understood the evolution of its story. What had once been a shattered dangerous substance now lay upon the beach, harmless, inert and beautiful after being tossed and rubbed by the real weather of the world. It had, with time, become a pastel memory of a useful vessel, to be carried, perhaps in a back pocket, and brought out and examined now and then. It was a relic of that special moment when the memory and the edge of the break softened and combined in order to allow preservation.

How long, she wondered, did it take, from the break on the rocks, through the storms of different seasons, to the change? When did the edges cease to cut?

That night he came in tired and heavy, followed by the smell of making things come to be. He spoke of the problems with the farm, of obstinate machinery that refused to function or of crops with inexplicable malformations – events that, even in the power of his stubbornness, he could never hope to control. And when he turned to look at her his eyes were like fresh broken glass: sharp, dangerous, alive. She answered him with kindness, though, knowing the storm ahead and then the softening of edges yet to come.

"There's storm glass on the beach," she said.

139

Joseph Boyden

For Now

Lexie hadn't been living here long at all when I asked her to go out. Maybe play a game of pool or have a drink, and she said yes, which made me happy. I said let's take my motorcycle and she said bikes are dangerous and I said we're all going to die anyway. That made her mad.

"There's snow on the ground, for chrissakes," Lexie said. "All I need is to catch a cold. You go ahead. I'll take a warm cab and meet you." And that's what we did.

I still think it was a ridiculous plan, considering we live in the same boarding house and The Guv'ner's Cue is only ten blocks away. You'd never guess, but as luck had it, I ended up hitting some black ice on Gerrard Street on the way home. I wrecked my BMW and got a bad road rash and now it's getting all infected. But we had a good time. I made her laugh. She really has a nice smile, even if she doesn't flash it enough. But she can't play pool worth a shit.

My name is Moose. It isn't my real name. My real

name is Raymond, but nobody's called me that since I was a baby. The first word out of my mouth was moose. My mom always joked that it obviously wasn't my size that warranted my name. It was my desire to be a patriotic Canadian baby. Actually I was only trying to say 'juice.' My mom started calling me Raymond again a year and a half ago when I found out I was positive. When I told her, all she could do was cry and say that my name was to blame. That I was always trying to live up to something bigger than I was and that's why I took so many chances and got in with the crowd I did. But that's not true. Anything you do in life's a gamble, and I guess you could say I rolled snake eyes. And here I am at the boarding house, still healthy and on the top, on the fourth floor.

It's a nice house, a sprawling Victorian, well over a hundred years old in Cabbage Town, one of the few truly hip places to live left in downtown Toronto. Lexie moved into the house and onto the third floor a couple of months ago. Soon as I saw her, I knew there was something special about her. It was just after New Year's and all I can say is she brightened the glum mood. You haven't been depressed until you've spent a January in Toronto. The wind is bitter cold off Lake Ontario, the sun's moved to Australia for a vacation, and streets and sidewalks are choked with grey slushy snow. It's definitely not motorcycle weather, although I admit I've been known to drive in less than ideal conditions.

People always say it's the depression of the holiday season that kills you, but I know different. It's that month after. Abe and Karl down on the first floor both went in mid-January, within two days of each other. Both left quiet as the whisper of their respirators. How else are you going to go, all junked out on morphine or Percodan? When I was young, I always pictured myself going in a high speed wreck, losing that tire hug on a hairpin, spinning out into a burnt rubber void. When I became tainted, I imagined the suck of the heroin void. But nobody wants to imagine it, a smell like paint thinner and cologne drifting into the first floor dining room in the middle of the ugliest month of the year. And that's when Lexie moved in with her locker of clothes and too many artsy pictures to fit in her little room and a squawky cockatiel in its antique bamboo cage. There was grumbling from the other boarders, I tell you, with the shifting of rooms and the movement up and down stairs of possessions: beds, the odd copy of the Bible or a Tibetan Book of the Dead, potted ferns, framed snapshots of the owner's face sandwiched in among friends or family, colourful bottles of pills. I got to keep my room so I kind of helped out where I could. I got to keep my room because I've not gotten sicker. Although she never speaks of it, Mrs. Bennigan – the woman who runs the house – keeps the healthy ones on the upper floors and the ones limited or bed-ridden down where they can still get to the dining and living rooms. Mrs. Bennigan says change is good for your heart and mind when she gets a new boarder or gets it into her head to move certain people to new rooms. But generally, you move onto a floor and begin the slow sink down to street level.

I have to admit that on moving day I helped out with Lexie's stuff more than anybody else's. She actually didn't have all that much, and I've never in my eight months here tried to forge any lasting relationships with the other boarders. People are either quiet or too talkative, and both make me uncomfortable. We'll talk at dinner or make fun of the same stupid TV shows, but I keep a life of my own. I'll go out to eat or have a beer and not worry about people at the next table sneezing or drafts blowing. And Lexie didn't talk too much or too little on the day she moved in – she would carefully listen to and repeat each of our names as she met us, then shake our hands gently, asking us all, "How are you doing?" – and, oh God, she had the most lovely, curly brown hair I've ever seen. She even laughed when I carried her antique bird cage up to the third floor and asked her what kind of bird it was and she said cockatiel and I said cocktail? I'd love one! Where and what time?

Like I was saying, we played some pool and I wiped out my bike on black ice, and now Lexie probably thinks I'm some kind of macho asshole who does stupid things because he's insecure. What do you do? I don't like sitting, so I ask Lexie out skating. "There's an outdoor rink," I tell her. "You know the one at City Hall. It isn't more than a five dollar cab fare and I'll gladly pick up the bill, if you care to join me."

"I haven't skated since I was a little girl," she says. "I don't even own a pair of skates."

"This is the first sunny day in a while," I say. "We'll bundle up and the rink people rent skates, and I'll pick up that tab too." Lexie hems and haws and I tell her the fresh air and sunshine will do her good. The ice is bumpy and slushy. Lexie's an ankle skater, for sure, her feet turned crooked. She kind of hops and steps. I get to hold her elbow and support her as we skate slow circles around the rink and look at all the hot shot kids zooming around, dodging old folks and rink attendants and the other ankle skaters. Lexie's breath explodes in foggy puffs as she laughs and tries to keep her balance. She holds onto me on the turns. There's not much wind because we're protected by the looming quarry grey Parliament buildings and oddly-shaped twin towers of City Hall.

"It's actually warm," Lexie says. She stumbles around in her cashmere coat and earmuffs. Finally we park on the heated bench, drink hot chocolate, and watch all the people going round and round. "It's weird to skate again," Lexie says. We follow the movement of an old couple gliding gracefully arm in arm. "Do you like living in the house?" she asks.

"Okay, I guess. You've probably seen I don't hang out with the others much."

"So why do you want to hang out with me?"

"I'm attracted to you," I say and jump up to skate fast on the ice, chasing the hot shot kids as the rink attendants shoot us nasty looks.

Mrs. Bennigan doesn't like the idea of Pete being in the house. "He's got dander," she tells Lexie at the dinner table. "All animals do. That's what people are allergic to." Others around the table listen carefully. Nancy and Michael nod in agreement. Todd and Mark and me shake our heads with Lexie.

"You can't keep your room properly ventilated," Mrs. Bennigan continues. "What with the cold weather and not being able to open your window for the draft ..."

I speak up. "Mrs. B," I say, "nobody's sneezing and the bird can actually say a few words. I like it around."

"Me too," say Todd and Mark.

"Jesus," Todd lisps. "It's not as if we'll simply drop dead because of the poor creature."

"Live and let live," adds Mark.

Lexie looks over at us. "Thanks fellas, but I can fight my own battles." That shuts us up. "Mrs. B, I'm not going to get rid of the bird. He's not a health hazard. I keep the cage clean. It's a simple cliché, but if the bird goes, I go." Lexie's got balls.

Mrs. B tries to diffuse things, but she doesn't want to give an inch. "If I notice people sneezing or itching, I'm going to have to ask you to find another home for the bird."

Lexie and me like to sit up late at night and talk. The living room is our meeting place long after everyone's sleeping. We lie on opposite ends of the couch and touch feet and look up at the high ceiling that catches the drifting light of passing cars. You'd never know it's March coming in like a lion when it goes out the same way. We whisper so Mrs. B doesn't hear us. She won't stand late night escapades. She's a good woman, worrying about us. I've tried to get up the courage to ask Lexie to one of our rooms to continue, but I'm kind of weak kneed around her.

Lexie asks, "What do you think comes later?" It's one of our favorites.

I say, "After this, it's the big blue. You pull on the wet suit. Take a last big breath and sink, sink, sink." I don't feel so hot tonight.

"Nuh uh. You don't swim with the fishes. You don't go to heaven either. If you're bad you become an earwig. If you've been neutral and a bore you become a pigeon. If you've been a good boy or girl and take vitamins daily you become a little child who grows up to be a healthy old person." It's a short game. When we play, we each get our one spiel and that's it. There's no use pushing further.

"Why won't you sleep with me?" My question catches us both off guard. Lexie doesn't answer. She climbs off the couch, and I hear her footsteps and little cough as she walks up the stairs. After a couple of minutes, I get up and follow. I open her door quietly and go lie beside her.

"That wasn't an invitation," Lexie says.

"I know," I say. I look around the room. The night light beside the bed makes everything look soft. No sharp edges on picture frames; the bottom corners of Lexie's single bed curve into darkness. Pete's big round cage in the corner is covered by a towel. Outside the window, it's snowing again.

"It's snowing again," I tell her with her back turned to me. I touch her head and bury my fingers in all the brown curls.

"Don't," she says.

One morning I wake early and decide to ask Lexie out for coffee. I can hear Mrs. B in the kitchen downstairs when I tiptoe to Lexie's room and knock gently until she answers. "Right now or in a couple of hours?" She sounds like I woke her up.

"The sun's shining," I say. "Let's get a jump on the day. Fresh air will do us good." I watch Lexie pad to the bathroom in her robe. Pete squawks from under the towel so I walk over and remove it. He squawks some more, then says, "Mornin'."

"Good morning," I answer, then whistle. He ruffles his feathers. I open the cage door and slowly put my hand in. He backs away in little hops. When my hand gets close enough, he pecks at it. I move my hand to try to touch him and he screeches and flaps himself hard all over the cage, white down flying all over the place. I close the door and talk softly to try to calm him. When Lexie returns, I'm sitting with my legs crossed on the edge of her bed, looking innocently out the window.

We walk up to Bloor and head west to The Second

Cup, past all the businessmen, the bicycle couriers, and the secretaries in pretty skirts and running shoes. It's the first day in weeks that hasn't been overcast. You can see the difference. The bounce in people's steps and the smiles from absolute strangers. At a booth by the window we cradle hot cups of coffee and watch people walk by.

"My T-cell count's fallen," Lexie says.

"How far?" I ask.

"Put it this way, Moose. A cold will kill me and our late night talks and walks outdoors and you making me crazy with your constant come-ons are not helping." She begins to cry. I go over and sit beside her and kiss her cheek. I can't stop. I kiss her forehead and her nose and eyes and lips and she keeps crying and begins to kiss me back until all we can do is sit and hold one another, making out like a couple of fourteen-year-olds.

"I'm going to the doctor and then to see my mother," Lexie says when we walk back to the house. "Meet me tonight in my room."

"I hate the word 'lesion'," Lexie says. "It's ugly. It sounds like legion, legions of the doomed, French Foreign Legion. There's nothing pretty in the word."

"There's a certain lesion in France," I say, "renowned for its hearty grape and beautiful women." I take off Lexie's shirt. "Don't be so paranoid. It's only a rash."

"I really was pretty once," she whispers. "Lots of boys wanted me. I guess you could say that was my downfall." I kiss her mouth and hold her tight when she tries to take my shirt off.

"What?" she asks. "You trying to be coy all of a sudden?"

"No. Your bird is watching us. He makes me nervous."

147

Lexie giggles and stands up, walks over in her panties to the cage. She's a thin vision in the shadows, her slight curves. "Good night, Pete," she says. She leans close to the cage and makes little kissing noises that Pete imitates.

All hell broke loose today. Mrs. B casually mentioned at breakfast that some boarders were switching rooms. Mrs. B didn't look up when she added that Lexie was going to the second floor without Pete. "He has to find a new home," Mrs. B said. Lexie locked her door and wouldn't come out. She wouldn't even let me in, so I took matters into my own hands. I sat down over coffee with Mrs. B. After an hour of deliberation, she agreed to conditionally let me move Pete to my room on a trial basis. "Anything, I mean anything goes wrong, the bird flies this coop, Moose."

"No worries, Mrs. B," I answered.

Lexie hates the second floor. "It's bullshit," she says. "As if I can't get up and down the stairs. As if. . . ." But I notice her hold her side when we walk down for dinner. I make Lexie eat everything on her plate. I sit in the back-yard on warm days with her and talk and listen to Pete yak. "I'm going to teach him how to say 'Set my people free'," I say.

"Hey bird," Pete answers.

"He learned to say 'Hey bird' without me meaning it," Lexie says. She looks like Joan Crawford today with her head wrap and big shades and pale complexion. "I'd walk by his cage all the time when he was young and new and say 'Hey bird.' That was before I named him." I want to ask her where the name Pete came from, but I'm worried it's an old boyfriend's name who got her sick or the name of her father who's never come to visit. We sit and enjoy the sun until it gets low enough that the evening wind comes. Tonight Lexie asks me to go out, out to a dance club for a drink and to watch people boogie and have a good time.

"The clock, she is a-ticking, Boy-o," Lexie says. "I want to get drunk, wasted drunk. Then we can stumble home and fuck till dawn."

"You're up for it? Really up for it?" My voice shakes.

"Now or never, Moose." What can I say to her? I'll hold your arm on the way in and carry you out? I won't talk about worry. She'll just call me a hypocrite nerd monster. I slick my hair back and pull my best red silk smoking jacket from the closet. There's an ancient joint, thin and dry, from my wild days, in the pocket. Lexie and me smoke and exhale out the bedroom window as I help her dress. Clothes pile up on the floor. She finally finds the right outfit. A flower-patterned dress with exotic birds peeking from the hem and a white faux fur coat. I lace her black combat boots for her.

"Demure yet forceful," I say.

"The pot made my stomach ache go away," she answers. We sit in the quietest corner we can find and bird watch. That's what Lexie calls it.

"Ooh, look at that pretty boy," she says, the bass pounding, the strobe lights blinking and swirling.

"Enough to make me sick," I say. "Look at him, king of the discotheque. I'm dyin' over hee-ah!" I shout in my best Jimmy Cagney. My words are swallowed up. We laugh at that, lean over and kiss hard.

"Bartender," I holler, "gimme a fancy drink for my girl. One of those things with an umbrella. And a beer for me." Lexie and me whoop it up in our seats during the fast songs when the bass is so pumped our asses vibrate in their chairs. I see a couple of lidded lanky boys prowling in a dark corner, kids in knee-length black leather coats that I ran with in the wild days. Still up to no good, cutting a deal in the black light by the bathrooms. They pretend not to see me so I rattle an empty bottle on the table.

"Midnight express, boys," I yell. "Mainline to Nirvana." Lexie laughs at that one. She's feeling no pain. We stumble out arm-in-arm, our ears ringing and faces flushed by alcohol.

"Oh, Darlin'," I say, "I only wish I still had my motorcycle. We'd whip up to the bluffs and look down at the lake. I'd take you on a fast ride through Kensington Market for a late night coffee."

"Promises, promises," Lexie answers. "Borrow somebody's bike. There's always tomorrow." But I can see her heart's not in it anymore. The thrill of the night is back at the dance club. Lexie hails a taxi with her New York whistle and I have half a mind to tell the cabby to ride us back to the club. I realize it's no use though, trying to chase down the feeling that won't be where we left it.

"You just gotta leave some things in the past," I say, my head in Lexie's lap in the back of our downtown cab.

She stares at me for a minute. "The night's not over," she says. "I want to spend what we got left with you and Pete up in my room." Lexie says her legs are tired, so I scoop her up and walk the one flight with her in my arms, banging walls with her dangling feet, the two of us giggling and me stopping every five steps to catch my breath. We're breathless. I don't know how we're not caught by Mrs. B, making all that racket. We're breathless.

Lexie's having trouble getting out of bed. For a while

I'd carry her down to dinner and to watch TV with me, but she's too sore now to be moved much. I sneak into her bed at midnight and hold her until dawn begins to break. Mrs. B is worried about the black baggage under my eyes and the fact I nap a lot during the day. "You have me worried, Moose," she says. "Your boyishness and general aura of conviviality is not what it used to be."

"I miss my motorbike," I tell her. Commando raids to Lexie's room with Pete under my sweater or T-shirt is the only way for the two to visit. I've considered taping his mouth shut when he puts up a stink.

"It's the chopping block for you, Petie ol' pal," I try to reason with him. "Mrs. B would pluck both our feathers." I sit by the window during these visits and watch summer stretch out all muggy over Toronto as Lexie and Pete chirp at one another. Pete moves from pulling and preening Lexie's thin hair to perching on her shoulder and kissing her ear. Some days Lexie's not too aware. She stares out the window empty-eyed and saying nothing. I just sit and watch the slow drip of her intravenous.

Other days she looks at Pete and smiles and says, "Change is good, Boy-o." She's always sure to let Pete know he's no pigeon. They give one another a couple of pecks on their respective beaks when visiting time's over. It really is a sweet thing to watch.

Mrs. B informed me at breakfast today that Lexie doesn't want me visiting anymore. "As you know, she's conscious less and less, Moose. But yesterday she woke up abruptly when I was changing her sheets. She told me in no uncertain terms. I'm sorry, Moose. I know it hurts, but she wants to be by herself now."

I don't believe Mrs. B. I slowly finish my toast and get up to leave. The other boarders remain silent. As I climb the stairs, Mrs. B stops me. "Moose," she says. "She doesn't want the bird visiting either." I just look down at her. "Don't fret," she continues. "Feathers in the bed, dear."

Pete's belligerent when I try to take him out of the cage. "We have to talk to Lexie," I tell him. "She's out of her head. We have to talk to her." I back away a few steps from the cage door. Pete stares into his mini-bird mirror, kissing and chatting to himself. I sit on the bed. Pete hops to the door, ready. When I make a move to stand he jumps and whirs his wings and flies quick and madly around and around the room. He darts to the window and bangs into the screen. He's groggy when I gently pick him off the floor. I kneel with him in my hands and rub his belly.

"It's okay, Pete," I tell him. "You're okay."

(In Memory of Muz)

Patrick Lane

Pale Light

Pale light through the windows. It fell upon the white floor, a living thing come from the night, the moon a far wandering. I watched it become thinner and thinner, a curved blade diminishing, the shadow of its other body a weight only the sky could hold. Swollen, it obliterated the stars as it passed to the mountains of the west, a dark belly held in arms of light.

I remember my mother holding her belly the same way when she carried her last child, my brother, five years after the war. I saw her standing back from the wringer washing machine, the piles of clean and dirty clothes on the slat bench, clasping her hands below her as if holding a stone. I watched her from the porch door and saw what was a mother, mine.

Like that, her tiredness; like those, her days.

The hours don't exist.

I lift her out of the past. Her bones are potsherds found in a till, fragments of time plowed under.

In the hospital room the only measure was her breath. Her hair was a fall of grey on the pillow, the colour of a heron's breast at dawn above the tide. I had come to be with her in death. There had been others die before her, too many, my brother with his skull full of blood crying crazy in his bed, the drowned girl I found in the run-off waters of the Nicola River, her body tangled in a net of roots and branches, Cut-throat trout lilting in her hair, the old Remittance man I helped bury up the North Thompson. I was barely a man back then, the back-hoe gouging the grave he would lie in, unnamed, unmarked, forgotten but for my going back years later and laying a stone where I thought his bones might be, thinking apology a remedy for grief.

Who can be forgiven?

My murdered father?

My Uncle Jack pushed me bodily into his coffin as he shouted at me, Kiss him! Kiss your father goodbye! It was the first I knew of love between men, Jack's tears, my struggle, the lipstick and powder on my father's face marking me, I think, forever.

And there were other deaths but what do they matter who watched his mother fail away? I'd seen the old ones walking in the park outside the hospital. They passed by with such slowness I could see through them to the trees and the towers of the city. The ocean's light turned them diaphanous, thin mist their shroud, bowed heads and tentative steps the measure of the lives they'd lost, the last to fail themselves. Once I reached out as if to touch a woman's hand and she stopped a moment and looked at me, O, from such a distance. No, not a stranger's hand, my mother's, and she rocked her head a moment as if to wonder who I was. I touched her hand and helped her back to the bench and sat her down.

What's wrong with you?

Her question old as life. A few weeks before she vanished, thin smoke, a frail mist rising.

A woman's hand, my mother's.

Who am I that I should write now of her death who carried me gentle in the waters of her womb? Too long ago to tell and today I'm older than my father and in ten years I'll be older than her and I'll know less and less until at last I'll know nothing, nothing at all. What did she know who blessed me at the end?

Blessing, warning?

Grief is a deep well. We dive into those waters until we become the rings that radiate from us, frail circles vanishing. I circle my grief like the poet said of his mother, quietly.

Years ago I watched a tidings of magpies surround a young gopher come early from his burrow. Unlike the old ones he didn't know to sleep through the cold and restless rose to the earth and the betrayal of the winter sun. The magpies trapped him outside his burrow. There were seven birds or nine, some uneven number, and they sported with the gopher. Confused, he seemed not to know why they held him there. Each time he tried to get to the safety of its burrow one or another of the birds would peck and drive him back.

Such play was theirs. I couldn't stay to watch the death and I didn't drive the birds away. Surely I am like that tidings of magpies. I won't let go what I hold. I play with it, my life a two-sided coin in a magician's hands. It seems at times I play with death.

I'm weightless, grief itself.

The last night before she slept she put her makeup on. At first I thought she'd become so deluded she didn't know if she was going to sleep or waking up and then I knew she was making herself beautiful. She'd told me she couldn't wait. I'll be with your father, she said. Your brother too. A lipstick slash across her lips, her hand trembling so she smeared it cross her cheek. And her hair. She had so little, just a few spare strands, yet she combed them carefully down over her forehead, brightly, sprightly, as she had all her life. Women and their hair. And rouge too on her cheeks, too much, but I knew her eyes had failed. What she saw in the tiny mirror I held up was a face as young and beautiful as she thought she'd always been.

As she was and would be.

Death eats us alive. I could see her skull. It was such a fragile thing, that bone cup I think held who she was. There was a time in the far past when people thought the soul lived in the groin and then they imagined it the heart. When did we decide upon the skull as a container for the soul? How far away from our bodies can we go until we lose sight of ourselves and think our souls reside outside us or don't reside in us at all.

I am of a people come to a soul-less place.

Who did I see lying on the bed in that hospital room where the last light of the moon shone pale through the window? What does a mother know when a child resides in her? Is there a moment when the soul arrives? Does a mother place her hands on her still-flat belly and feel through her palms that first arrival? To have a soul within a soul?

What does a man know?

I feel at times a man balanced on canes at the edge of a park, some shriven, wreckless thing, someone last, lost, left behind: a man who doesn't. I watched an old one in the park one day. Was she beside me on the bench? No, I was alone. I know he stood by the far trees and like the trees he swayed with the wind come off the sea. It wasn't a heavy wind, just some light touch of air come weaving. He was still there when I left to go back inside the hospital and I wondered as I walked away if anyone knew he was there, if anyone was going to come and take him to wherever he was to go. Perhaps he saw around him angels in the shape of magpies, a tidings of things to touch him to his rest.

I wish my father had lived long enough to die.

I wish my mother had my father longer.

But what are wishes but luck gone wanting? I seem to begin everything with a question. Perhaps there are only questions. But there must be more? Surely there's only a presence of things for lack of thinking farther than I can. Back then I lost what lay before me, but what made me think she was mine to lose?

I am bewildered.

A year before her death I went into the mountains to lose myself. I walked back into the bush until the hills became rocks, the creeks thin rivulets born from the fingers of glaciers as they retreated through tumbled scree. There were no trails but for bear and mountain goat. I sat at the beginning of water. I saw the birth of rivers rise in the far mountains. I knelt on the ground and leaned my face into first water and I drank from a clear pool, took into my body what once was snow.

I'm made at times of ice.

I camped by a nameless creek and made my fire. I lay myself down on pine boughs under the stars and thought I was the only man there was, I was that lonely. There were so many stars I thought there must be a god for what else could have caused them to flare so willingly. I

157

think I'm that old man in the park.

The other women in the ward were far away in sleep. My mother was awake. We didn't speak. Her bright eyes stared at me, curious. She had a quizzical look, the kind that wonders. What do the dying see? On my knees was The Old Curiosity Shop. I brought it thinking it was the favourite of his books. She loved Dickens. She'd read him aloud to me and my brothers when we were children: A Tale of Two Cities, Bleak House, Hard Times, the rest. We lived those pages of the far past, that other, older century, the nineteenth after Christ. She reveled in words, loved the detail of a world that was still in reach when she was but a child.

Who was she back in the days of the little girls?

I remember what she was like when I was a boy. The time she clasped her hands under her belly in the kitchen when she stepped back from the washing machine and the tubs and held her last, my brother a stone in her arms. What did she think as she held his body in herself? Why can I see her?

She was tired of her sixteen-hour days and nights of looking after a family on little money, a wood stove, a laundry tub for baths, linoleum on the floor curled at the edges where it met the walls and worn away under the pine table where we sat to eat the food she made.

She paused for breath.

I don't remember her laughing. The only thing she would smile for was a camera and that was a thin smile, deceptive in its slight. It was as if she knew something the rest of us didn't. She'd a magpie look, curious and playful, strangely, cruelly kind.

She closed her eyes when I read to her. The woman across from her never moved. She'd been in a coma a long time. The ward cat slept in the hollow of her legs and stared at my mother and me. I didn't look back. I wrote a poem the night her husband slept with her.

> The man in the hospital who, late
> in the night, the women, sick, asleep,
> took off his clothes, folding them neatly
> and laying them down, the shirt and pants,
> the socks and underwear, and the shoes
> side by side beside the white chrome chair,
> in a room with only a small light
> burning above each bed, lifted
> the covers and lay down
> beside his wife who had not wakened
> for two years from the coma, and
> placing his arm across her breasts,
> his leg upon her leg, closed his eyes,
> silent, still, the breathing of his wife,
> his arm rising and falling with her life
> while the ward cat who would sleep
> with only her, watched from
> the foot of the bed, one ear forward
> and the other
> turned to the sounds of the distant city.

I looked at that woman on her bed. She had no visitors I saw but him that once. I think she was alone and whatever family there was had given up on her. That man said nothing to me, so intent he was on love. It seemed I wasn't there at all. The ward cat knew. Like the cat was the old woman in her sleep. Like a magpie my mother. Like that man am I.

I'm sick to death of death. There was a time a man would hire women to wail for him. They'd come in their long dresses and black shawls and sit in a circle. They'd sit and knit, talk among themselves as women do, but when death came they'd rise up and howl as if with their bodies they could cry all grief away. Is that what death is, some god come calling? Where were such women that I might have hired them? Would they be called a grief of women in the way magpies are a tidings, crows a murder, orphans an abandonment? Is this what I do here, list things in their gatherings?

I'm sick of me.

I remember the night I left the bar at The Cecil Hotel. It was three years after my father's death, three years after the poets deserted the place at the end of the Sixties and The Cecil became a country-and-western bar with strippers and pole-dancers, addicts and drunks, pimps and johns and whores. I was drunk and stoned and tired of booze and whores. I walked down to False Creek where the ocean never moved. It's odd to think how I folded my clothes and placed them on a rock. How neat I was. I sank a dozen times and each time my body rose again to the surface, refusing to let go its hold on things. I sank again and then again, each time thinking this was surely the last. At the end I lay on my back upon the water and stared up at the stars.

Death doesn't come to us easy. It's us who must come to death. We're welcome then.

I think my mother was welcome.

I think she was good at death who wasn't good at life. Why do I say that? God knows, she gave birth to us three and raised us through the war and then two more, my sister, my little brother.

I saw her hold her belly in her arms as if her last was what she must endure. There were no more. Old Doctor

Alexander cleaned her out. He promised her that when she asked for an abortion. You have this one and I'll make sure you have no more. I can hear him talking quiet in the kitchen. I was at the porch door listening. I think at times I was some kind of ghost child, a spirit sent to keep close watch on her. She never told my father what she did. Five was enough and she was tired of birth. He came hard, my brother, born at the end like that. Eleven pounds he was. She told me he split her open when he came. He almost killed me, she said.

I read to her there in the night. The past came stuttering, glimpses, bits and pieces of a film stitched together every which way. There's no order to me. There never was. I remember too much. I remember wishing my brain would die. I remember wishing as I read from Dickens, her eyes closed, her hair combed just right, the lipstick crooked on her lips, her breathing light. I reached out and placed my hand upon her breast and held it there. I felt the bone cage move. I swear her lips couldn't lift a feather. She was a whisper made of silk so strange as to be made by the ghosts of worms.

All of them came back to me. It was as if I watched the dreams she had. As if what was in her mind became mine and I could see back through the war to some other, earlier time, the Thirties and Twenties, her in a jangly dress, my father with his foot up on the running board of a Model A Ford, a cigarette in his hand, a cigarette in hers, the two of them young and wild. And later, The Sullivan Mine and my father coming down the rocky trail to her, two children, me not born, not yet, her belly swollen. Did she stand alone and hold me like the crescent moon holds night?

I swear I'll kill my sight.

She reared up from the bed and grabbed my wrist. Her tiny hand just skin stretched over bone, fine vellum pulled across thin sticks. Shining there, her eyes what the almost dead have, a bright and terrible burning, and she said to me as if to admonish, as if to warn me of my only life, as if to make of praise another kind of calling: At every turn there's always something lovely!

So I sit and hold onto what death knew and knowing gave to me that I might turn my life, to what? O, mother, who is it I mourn? Whose death did I wait for in that room? I'm alive in a kept silence and I turn and turn again upon your words and wait upon my wanting. You died and I have nothing here but words. I make of them a memory to you who sang to me and sing to me still, your voice as bright as the sharp points of the moon before its gone, that blade of light that holds the heavens, crescent-shaped, like two arms holding on to what it knows, curved around a belly where a stranger grows.

Rona Altrows

Silent Partner

Mitchell has nodded off. He's got his mother's long lashes, and eyelids so delicate they are almost transparent. His eyes race back and forth under those lids. I think that means he is dreaming. What do you dream about when you've only been out of the womb for four months? The warmth of your mother's full breast? The sweetness of her milk? The ring of your father's laugh? What would a nightmare be about? Being left alone. Filling your pants up at both ends and getting cold, then hungry. Crying your lungs out for help.

When Mitchell stirs, I unclasp the baby car seat he is sitting in, gently pull away the straps and lift him into my arms. How can a person be so light? I feel honoured that my customer Renata has asked me to keep an eye on him while she is in the fitting room. Many opportunities for me to grow as a human being occur here at Marjorie's Lingerie. Like this one.

When I was a girl, my mother gave me child-rearing tips. She didn't have an agenda; it was just in her nature to pass on knowledge. When you hold your baby, hold him

163

close, she told me. Which is what I'm doing with Mitchell right now, although he is not mine.

He is pursing his tiny mouth, relaxing it, pursing again. I wonder if he is getting hungry.

"He seems to be thinking about mealtime," I call out to Renata.

"Out in two secs," she answers.

Now there's no doubt. With his hands and lips, Mitchell is searching out my breast. Sorry, little buddy, can't help you out with that. I give him the baby finger of my left hand. It's a poor substitute but he sucks with gusto, making the best of an imperfect situation. I'm afraid I may have done the wrong thing, sticking my finger in his mouth. Germs and all that. Then again, I read in a magazine that it's useful for kids to be exposed to germs when they are babies and toddlers. Otherwise they will get sick more often than their classmates once they reach school age. Something about developing immunities.

Renata emerges from the fitting room and says she is happy with the nursing bra she tried on. We do a trade. I hand her Mitchell and she hands me the bra. In a minute she'll have both.

"Can you use a package of the disposable nipple pads?" I ask. "You slip them right into the cups of the bra and wear them between feedings to absorb leakage."

"Sure," she says, and I ring in the sale for both items.

"I wish my mother were more like you," she says, as she signs the credit card receipt.

Now we are entering dangerous waters. I know Renata's mother, Paula; she has been shopping here at Marjorie's Lingerie for twenty-plus years. Paula is a difficult customer – pushy, petty, sometimes rude. She once picked out a nightie that suited her perfectly and I told her so; her answer was "I don't need your compliments." I don't know why she keeps shopping here and often I wish she wouldn't. It's hard to believe that a sweetheart like Renata is her child. But here's the thing: Renata is about to slag her mother and even though I sympathize with her, I can't show favouritism for one customer over the other. The best thing to do right now is to listen, even harder than I have done before.

"My mother is out of her mind," Renata says. "She interferes in every single thing to do with Mitchell. She hates the name we picked for him. She pushes us to put him on solid food right away. She tells me I don't support his head properly when I pick him up. She insists I switch to a different diaper rash cream. Criticism, criticism, criticism ... she pounds me with it."

I do feel for Renata but I need to measure my response. What are the right words? I think of something my own mother would say when she was faced with this kind of scenario. You tell the truth and it is up to your listener if she wants to hear beyond your words.

"I'm sure your mother means well," I say.

"Why can't she be more like you? Renata asks. "You're so non-judgmental. You've never questioned anything about how I take care of my baby."

"I don't see you and Mitchell often and when I do, we're not together for long. Also, we're not related. It's apples and oranges."

"I guess you're right," she says. I can see she is a little disappointed I didn't jump to her defence. I would have liked to do that, too, but to be loyal to both customers, I can't go beyond a certain point on this topic.

Mitchell bawls. He is not too happy with the way his

mother and I have set our priorities over the past few minutes. He's been hungry, but now he is famished. He is letting out long, piercing howls with a tremolo. I've learned the meaning of that vibrating cry from having so many mothers and babies in the store over the years: Feed me now.

"Do you think your son might like to dine in one of our fine fitting rooms?" I ask.

"That'd be great," Renata says. "Thank you so much."

While she breast-feeds Mitchell in privacy, I do a bit of dusting. It's a Wednesday morning and nobody else is here at Marjorie's Lingerie, so the moment is right for this chore. There's lots to do. Dust accumulates fast everywhere in Calgary's dry climate, no matter how careful you are about cleaning. As I reach the feather duster up to a shelf top, my mind wanders to the early days of my marriage, thirty-two years ago, when Henry and I discussed whether to start a family. We didn't dwell on it, though. We were having a lot of fun as a couple and we used birth control almost without thinking about it. Nothing fancy, just your basic rubbers. They say some men complain about the feel of condoms. Not Henry. We both had plenty of juice. A sheaf of latex was not going to get in our way.

But when I reached thirty-three, I began to get nervous about running out of babymaking time. We had long talks, weighed pros and cons, tried to visualize ourselves in the mom and dad roles. We joked that Henry would be a good explainer and I would be a good entertainer for our children, because he had a logical mind and I knew how to tell a funny story. But looking back, I don't think we were clear in our heads about what we wanted. Our conversations were about how we would carry out our jobs as parents, how our lives would change. Us adjusting to kids, that's what we concentrated on. We never speculated much about the kids themselves or how they might feel living with us. That was the big gap in our thinking, only we never realized it.

We so-called Tried, but after a year, I hadn't conceived. I got anxious over the failure. Why wasn't it working? I thought we must be missing something. At various times I suggested we try different positions, different days in my cycle. We even experimented a bit with diet. I had read that prunes and eggs might work, so we went through a stage when we had a lot of omelettes with prune compote for dessert. We got mighty sick of all those eggs and the prunes led to diarrhoea, so we stopped. Henry went along with whatever I wanted and stayed cheerful. I think he just wanted me to be happy again and would do anything within reason to make that happen. I completely lost sight of the reason for what we were doing. For me, the whole project became about getting pregnant, not the happy prospect of bringing up a child. I started taking B Vitamins and drinking eleven cups of chamomile tea every day to try to relax. Once again I found myself living on the toilet.

Meanwhile, my periods kept coming. Every time it happened, I was relieved, and that reaction confused me even more. I started having daily talks with myself about whether the babymaking project made sense. If I wanted so badly to become a mother, why did I secretly celebrate every four weeks when I found blood on my panties? Maybe I was afraid of something – pregnancy or birth or raising a child. Or was I just in denial, and did I really wish failure on the baby project?

Henry was kind and caring, but not much help in

167

working this problem out. He had a lot to say when we talked about fishing or politics or his work in accounting or mine in selling and managing. He was full of suggestions on how not to take stress home from work, how to motivate employees, how to deal with impossibly difficult people. He could talk forever about the joys of poker, the ignorance of his two sisters who hated me, the way to percolate a perfect pot of coffee. But when it came to the babymaking project, Henry just let me drive and, except to calm and reassure me, he pretty well held his tongue. He was the silent partner.

When I turned thirty-five, I sat down with him and said I thought we should stop Trying for a while. I was exhausted and mixed up because of all the failure and especially because of my relief at the failure. Henry said fine and we went back to using birth control. I never saw him behave that passively about anything else in our marriage.

We never did go back to Trying. The subject of babies versus no babies came up occasionally, but as I moved into my late thirties, the question bothered me less. It was one of those things you don't resolve a hundred percent, but after a while you sense how it's bound to go.

Sometimes I get curious about what would have happened if we had Tried again and hit the baby jackpot. After all, I lost Henry only twelve years into the marriage. He was in a terrible car crash and died of his injuries nine long days later. If we had had a child together, maybe that would have brought me some comfort.

It's possible. But maybe that child would have had constant nightmares because of losing his father when he was little. Once he reached school age, he would have felt different and set apart from his classmates because he had suffered a loss they couldn't understand. Then they would start treating him as if he were crazy and that would only add to his loneliness. Besides, where would he have found a male role model? I'd be too affected by grief myself to go new-daddy shopping. Anyway, chasing men has never been part of my nature. I'd have to be both parents to our son, and who knows if I would have been up to the challenge? Probably not. So our boy would be a struggler all his life. What a prospect.

If Henry had lived a normal life span, our son might have been okay. But then in his old age, Henry would get Alzheimer's, which is what had happened to his own father in his last years. Our son helps out with his care but there is nothing we can do to prevent Henry's mental deterioration. Then, long after Henry and I are dead, our son comes down with Alzheimer's. He has the early onset kind and by the time he is fifty-four, he can no longer read or button up his own shirt. Gradually he loses the power of speech. He lives in a special care institution that smells of dying brains. At twilight each day he becomes agitated and paces back and forth in his tiny white room. A dozen times he has wandered off the hospital grounds and been brought back by police. The illness grows worse by the month and yet his heart keeps pointlessly beating. Our son finally does not know that he exists.

That's not a future I would want for any child of mine.

I enjoy being around babies. I do. Not the same way as my friend Doreen Lockhart, who goes gaga every time she is in the presence of anybody less than two years old. She has a baby granddaughter, Madison. We can't go anywhere, Doreen and I, without her needing to make a quick stop at a children's clothing store to pick up a new outfit for Madison. Doreen says she has never gotten over her babyitis. Each time she sees an infant or toddler, she yearns for another of her own. Here she is, over sixty, wanting to face another pregnancy. The feeling soon passes but while she's got it, it's real.

Renata and Mitchell come out of the fitting room. Mitchell's head is lolling and his eyes are half open. He looks like a perfectly content drunk.

"Can I give him one more hug before you go?" I ask.

"Of course," Renata says.

He feels soft and beautiful in my arms.

Will Ferguson

Pots & Pans

Here is an example of the difference between men and women. I was sprawled out on the couch the other day, eating Pringles straight from the can (I like 'em fresh) and reading an inflight magazine from trips long passed, when I came across the following factoid: "The last $3 bill in Canada, dated 1886 and featuring the portrait of Queen Victoria, was issued by the St. Stephen's Bank of New Brunswick."

Needless to say, I found this absolutely fascinating.

"Listen to this honey," I said as she was making supper, changing the baby, sweeping the floor and checking the oil in the car – all at the same time, while juggling a pea and a bowling ball.

"Listen to this," I said, a tad more impatiently. "The last $3 bill in Canada was issued in St. Stephen."

"So?" she asked.

So? We were living in St. Andrews, New Brunswick. St. Stephen was just down the road from us. "Don't you find that fascinating?" I asked.

Of course she didn't. But I'll bet if had I told a guy, he

171

would have been agog. I'll bet if I called up my friend Sam we could have discussed it for hours, probably over beer. Hopefully over beer.

The point being, womenfolk are different from the rest of us. I'll give you another example. My wife and I used to have this agreement: when one person cooks, the other person washes the dishes. We take turns.

The problem is, my wife loves to cook. Me? Not so much. So my wife makes meals that involve at least 14 separate stages, and as a result, I end up washing every pan, plate, and utensil in our house when it's her turn to cook. I end up washing dozens of pot lids – more lids than pots. Where's the logic in that? My wife rummages around in our back cupboards and finds pots and pans I didn't even know we had, as though she were conjuring them into existence just so I'll have to wash them.

We alternate our cooking days as well, which means our menu plan runs something like this:

MONDAY: Spaghetti. TUESDAY: Lemon chicken with garlic sauce and gently sauteed mushrooms. WEDNESDAY: Spaghetti. THURSDAY: breaded cutlets with caesar salad and tossed Thai vegetables. FRIDAY: Spaghetti. SATURDAY: Smoked salmon in a light hollandaise sauce with yellow peppers and a side of sesame spinach set on fire in a dramatic flambé followed by individually peeled grapes and glacier-chilled strawberries. SUNDAY: Spaghetti.

I tell you, if my wife cooks spaghetti one more time...

I'm kidding of course. My wife doesn't make the spaghetti. I do. My repertoire also includes Kraft Dinner, Kraft Dinner Supreme (i.e. Kraft Dinner with hot dogs cut into it), Kraft Dinner with Parmesan Cheese Sprinkled on Top, Kraft Dinner Deluxe (i.e. Kraft Dinner with really expensive hot dogs cut into it) and Kraft Dinner Surprise (i.e. Kraft Dinner with Hot Dogs That Are Way Past the Expiry Date).

Lately, when it's my turn to cook, I've been suggesting that maybe instead we go out for –

"Yes!" says my wife, grabbing her jacket. "I'll call the babysitter."

At the last restaurant, I breezily ordered the special without asking what it was. (As a man, I am trained to make decisions quickly and without waiting for all pertinent information. It's a knack we have.)

The waiter brought out a plate of spaghetti.

At least I know what to tip in a situation like this: a nice big shiny $3 coin.

S.K. Johannesen

The Artist of the Prayer Room

We were all late children, our parents older Norwegians of austere pietist views. Some of us had older siblings. These older siblings married one another and adopted the culture of the parents. But their adolescence was from before the war. We grew up in the late forties and early fifties, and experimented with lipstick and cigarettes. We rode the subway. To Coney Island, and to "the city," which meant Central Park, The Museum of Natural History, Hayden Planetarium, Greenwich Village, sometimes The Cloisters, the Frick. We rode the Staten Island ferry.

There were crushes, and much speculative intrigue of a romantic nature, but we had no money and were not welcome in one another's houses. Outer clothing in those days was stiff and heavy and smelled in winter, and female underwear still a forbidden zone of crinolines and vests and garter clips, so we engaged mainly in kissing, a clumsy and unpleasant affair of chapped lips and dried spit on cold faces. This was anyway an exclusively winter sport, connected with Sunday afternoons after Sunday

174

school and church. In the summer, Sunday school disbanded, church attendance fell off, and the gang dispersed to camp, to family cottages, to relatives in the country, to summer jobs, or, for those of us whose parents had neither cars nor cottages, to the damp chlorinated squalor of the swimming pool.

What we lacked in sexual experience we made up for in psychological games of exquisite complexity and cruelty. The master of these games was one of the pastor's several children, all of whom were clever and knowing and whose position made them uncomfortably exposed yet socially powerful. The tension between these things destroyed one of them, made at least two others oddly winsome and chastened characters later in life, but combined in the case of my friend Leo to make of him a perfect monster of snobbery, manipulation and calculated insult.

He had got hold of the then-fashionable lingo of "complexes," whose diagnostic traces were revealed to Leo in behaviour that common sense would have suggested meant the opposite. Was someone assertive or confident in an opinion or judgment? Clearly they were compensating for deep feelings of inferiority. Was another insecure or confused or feeling persecuted and weepy – often as not from Leo's bullying? As plain as anything this was due to secret assumptions of superiority.

Leo was, in addition, master of techniques of wrong-footing. He could maintain a perverse and contrary position on some question, say, of where we were to go for the afternoon – whether to the museum to see the bog people, who were naked, even though they looked like rubbed wood in their glass cases, or to Clove Lake to rent rowboats – to the point of driving the rest of us to exasperat-

175

ed rebellion and not a few tears – especially among those of us with either superiority or inferiority complexes – then switch sides abruptly, leaving us stranded, foolish, impotent in our exasperation, and Leo of course with the upper hand.

Leo left Brooklyn with his family when we were all about thirteen years old, and that was the end of the gang as it had been. Some families moved to Long Island. People left the church to join other sects, or, what was worse, formed splinters of their own. When this happened, which was frequent in the 40s and 50s, we could not henceforth speak to those people or to their children. We divided up along lines of money and culture and aspirations and of course of sex; the easy camaraderie of the subway rides to zoos and museums and the innocent and promiscuous kissing on front steps ended, and gave way to best friends and serious romances and the pull of the different high schools and colleges we went to. We did not, as the older brothers and sisters had done, marry people within the closed circle of families.

When I met Leo again we were both in mid-career, he was in publishing, I was a university lecturer, we were both divorced and remarried, both with grown children.

I had flown to LaGuardia from Toronto and rented a car, and having appointments in Cape Cod and in Brooklyn, had decided to cross the Sound from Port Jefferson, drive to the Cape and, coming back, take the ferry from New London to Orient Point, and so on to the city. This meant traversing the length of Long Island on a Sunday morning, with little traffic and only the evocative place names for company: Smithtown, Babylon, Ronkonkoma, Valley Stream. Places of summer jobs, ancient picnics, places people had disappeared to.

The meeting with Leo was a disaster from the beginning. I was astonished to learn that he remembered me chiefly with resentment. When we met at the church I showed him an old photo of the two of us. Ten-year-olds, arms across one another's shoulders. He noticed, with rancour, that I had been taller than him. I took him and his new wife to dinner at the last Norwegian restaurant in Brooklyn. The new wife disliked the food, Leo resented that I had spoken to his mother before she died, and resented that, as a consequence, I had important things to tell him about his parents and about his mother's last days.

Foolishly, I invited them to spend a weekend with us in Ontario. They came later that summer and Leo and I had a chance to speak privately one night after the theatre.

He thought I had been a threat to him when we were children. We had been rivals, it turned out. Rivals above all, he said, to my surprise, for the attentions of our friend Nikki. Nikki and I, he intimated, were the only ones he thought of as worthy opponents, the "intellectuals," as he put it – absurdly – in our crowd. Then he insinuated that there had been something more than kissing between him and Nikki, maybe some degree of petting beyond what was usual in the subways and on the front steps in winter, maybe even something more than that.

It seemed to me undignified to press the point. What did it matter after all those years?

Nevertheless, this clumsy attempt to gain an advantage in some imaginary struggle we were supposed to be engaged in, brought back in the following weeks a flood of memories. Pink frilly dresses with bows, the neatly fitted cloth coats and little hats of a twelve-year old girl. In those days she was still called Anniken. Later, I walked her to her door and we sat and talked on her stoop until her father rapped on the window and called her inside.

I recalled that Nikki had been a beauty, a wide down-turned mouth like a Swedish actress, lively quizzical eyes. Nikki was also willful, and imaginative. She had written me teasing notes, more than once, from the time we were children, that we would live together when we were old in the "gamlehjem," the Norwegian old-people's home, a place near Thirteenth Avenue, where church picnics were sometimes held because of the extensive grounds, and where we were startled as children by the wrinkled faces and vacant stares and the starched mob-caps of old women sitting in the windows.

Then another distinct memory, from later.

We must have been seventeen or eighteen; the last time I saw her until the encounter I am about to relate. I walked her home from some event at church, as when we were children, and sat for many hours on her stone stoop next to an area with a rose-of-Sharon bush enclosed in iron palings. We talked about our experiences and plans. The only thing I remember was a rigmarole of a story about a man from work – an office in the city somewhere – who had taken her to a rooftop party. She drank too much. She remembered staying on. Someone fondling her breasts or stroking her belly – I don't remember which it was. And being undressed. Nor could I remember what the point of it all was supposed to be, or what I felt then it all meant. Flaunting? Teasing? Mocking? I only know that I felt a peculiar desolation. A conviction that I was out of my depth. Anger at my own lack of experience.

As I said, I did not see Nikki again until about fifteen years ago, the summer after I saw Leo for the last time.

Nikki now lived in a small city in south-central Pennsylvania. Not really so far from Brooklyn: Verrazano, Goethals, the New Jersey Turnpike, the Pennsylvania Turnpike to the Reading exit. Four hours on a pleasantly hot summer afternoon with the air-conditioning on and the radio full of Oliver North and Admiral Poindexter; it was the summer of Iran-Contra.

I called Nikki from the Treadway Inn outside of town. I said I was passing through and had a free evening. A breezy intelligent voice with traces of a Brooklyn accent said she was going out to dinner with a friend, but come over, we could all go out together. I demurred. She said well, it is a woman friend, so it's no bother. She said her daughter would come over and show me the way.

I asked what the daughter looked like.

Some jokey asides with another female voice in the background, then Nikki came back on.

"She's driving a blue Toyota. She says she looks like a scumbag."

Nikki was well off. Divorced from a society doctor, a gynecologist. A son, who was not at home, was something in films. The beautiful daughter, who liked dropping words like "scumbag," pursued a course at a local college. When Nikki came down to meet me she was wearing a too-youthful taffeta skirt, perhaps borrowed from the daughter. I said she hadn't changed a bit, which was partly true. The same ashy-blonde hair, now more art than nature, the same down-turned mouth. In the old snapshots Nikki had always worn a scowl. I had come to think of her this way. She had two strong lines that ran downward from the corners of her mouth. A determined face. Laughing eyes, blue-grey. Not quite what people think of as Scandinavian, but to those of us who grew up

179

among them, a very Norwegian face: A certain tautness over the cheekbones, the slightly jutting jaw, a faraway look in unguarded moments.

The town-house she lived in was a smart horror of flounces and bad pictures. She walked around her well-appointed little city. We talked about the past. She had a great fund of stories from the old days, stories from the hidden world of women: the two sisters seduced by their step-father, a pillar of the church, an elder and former missionary to India; the mother of one of our gang who flushed a foetus down the toilet to protect an older sister; the couple who had sex regularly during church services, slipping out and dashing off to his family's house in his MG sports-car. Nikki tried to project a coarse relish in this tittle-tattle.

She also kept dropping hints about a young boyfriend – his youthfulness was insisted upon – a carpenter, with a pickup truck and toolbox. I felt the old desolation beginning to creep over me.

I went back to the Treadway Inn to shower and change. Nikki picked me up later, and we went to get her friend. The friend's name was Rhoda and she lived next door to the house where Nikki had lived with her husband. Rhoda was also an abandoned wife, although still in possession. Seeing her old house was clearly upsetting for Nikki. It was an ugly brick thing, and Nikki had in her time put on an addition with appalling faithfulness to the dull original and its graceless windows. Now someone was making it over again, with the addition of screening-walls with port-hole openings. "Post-modern," Nikki said disapprovingly. Nikki regretted the grand fund-raising lawn parties she used to throw, and all the friends she used to have. She told me how she had been cheated out of this house by her husband. Nikki had stuck with him through years of infidelity, and neglect and helplessness. When it came time to turn this around, he got expensive psychotherapy and she got drugs. In the middle of this therapeutic regime he left her anyway, landing her in an asylum to dry out, with her kids at home with no food.

We had a pleasant dinner. Rhoda was taking a course at the local college. We talked about that, and about Ollie North. Nikki and I tried to explain to her about growing up in a Pentecostal church, and about speaking in tongues, and about being Norwegian, some of which was very funny. After we dropped Rhoda off, we went to Nikki's house and talked until late.

Nikki remembered her childhood as a happy one. Her parents were in love, and there were many intimations of a robust sex life between her parents. Her father had been a master machinist. He made lamps out of artillery shells as a hobby, she said, although Nikki does not own one. She would like to. A wealthy aunt kept Nikki and her sister supplied with expensive dresses. Nikki remembered this still with a keen and childlike pleasure. Also the summer holidays paid for by this same aunt.

Her sister, Nikki said, does not remember her childhood in quite this same light. She seems mainly to remember her father as the ogre people commonly remember strict parents to be. Nikki saw an irony in this, as the sister is still a born-again Christian and Nikki is not.

Nikki remembers her father through the filter of her experience of marriage. Her father, in her view, for all his strictness was adequate in a way her husband wasn't. Her father gave his wife his full affection, indulgently, without reserve. She thought that was what a real man did. Although Nikki thought that her childhood was, on the whole, a happy one, she was resentful about the church, and told me an interesting story.

Her father believed that while it was true as a general principle that one mustn't lie, one might tell a lie under certain circumstances – to protect a friend, for example, or to earn a livelihood. In this spirit, Nikki had not only found herself a job for which she had to lie about her age, but had agreed with her boss, in order to cover the inconvenient fact that she looked too young, to wear lipstick at work, although this was strictly forbidden by the rule of the church.

As chance would have it, she was spotted wearing lipstick downtown by an elder of the church, a thick-headed reformed drunk whose own daughters flouted freely the spirit of the dress codes. If lipstick was taboo, they used heavy face powders. They wore no earrings, but bought flashy necklaces, bracelets – even anklets. If dresses must have demure sleeves that covered the shoulders, their hemlines crept provocatively above the knee. This much-hated pillar of respectability duly reported to the members-only business-and-communion meeting held monthly in the church basement that Nikki was seen wearing lipstick in public. I don't recall what she told me was the immediate consequence of this. No doubt a solemn warning about her witness before the world, and the perils of vanity, and the danger of backsliding.

Some while after this – a year or more, she said – Nikki was at a party for another girl in the church, a typical sort of 50s wedding shower with a tissue-paper throne for the guest of honour and small gifts of house wares and the like on display, and pot-luck refreshments. At the end, as people were leaving, someone reported five dollars missing from a purse. When this came to the attention of the elders, it was remembered that Nikki, of those present, had most recently come to their attention for discipline. A person who would wear lipstick would certainly steal. Nikki was confronted and given the lie direct. The pastor himself convened a sort of kangaroo court and tried to bluster her into a confession. They failed to break her. Nikki remembers that her mother stood by her, and told the elders in a trembling voice that her Anniken was a good girl, and would not steal five dollars or tell lies.

Nikki saw the whole structure of power in the church as built on intimidation and fear. On the one hand were the bullying elders, among whom she insisted were outrageous cases of concealed incest, insanity and violence. On the other hand were the old women, whose lives were spent hugging and rocking themselves in self-pity and regret, with those peculiar, sharp, in-taken Norwegian sighs, lines of weariness and quiet despair permanently stamped on their faces. As she talked, Nikki imitated these gestures and intonations to perfection. More than any of us in our circle, Nikki and her sister had grown up with Norwegian as the primary household language, and she had a genius for accents, but with a touch of hysteria that went beyond parody. The image of the rocking and self-hugging old ladies was clearly a terror for her, the nightmare she lived with. All this cast an interesting, and poignant, light, I thought, on Nikki's suburban appearance and demeanour, the brittle American middle-age she had chosen.

It also brought to mind again the odd idea she had when we were children, the one that we would meet in the gamlehjem when we were old. A forgotten detail of this fantasy came to me: she used to say that we would dig a tunnel between the old ladies' part and the old men's part, and sneak visits to one another.

Then yet another memory, sharp like old cheese.

The building used by the church for meetings was a former synagogue, the ornate wooden ark left in place at the front and serving now to house the baptismal tank, and Jesus in large gothic letters in gilt added to its pediment.

In the basement, in a bit of left-over space between the boiler room and the kitchen, the elders had constructed what came to be called simply the prayer room: a charmless, windowless, carpeted room with no furnishings or decoration, only a built-in kneeling bench running all around the irregular shape of the room.

This unprepossessing place was held to be the nerve centre for the entire spiritual project of the congregation. It was where pastors and evangelists went for inspiration, kneeling before an open Bible in prayerful attitude. Where whole nations of the heathen were converted by the heroic intercessions of a handful of elderly female prayer-warriors. Where the young people repaired after Sunday evening services in order to achieve, under the tutelage of watchful brothers and sisters, the Baptism in the Holy Ghost, the crowning initiation into adulthood and full membership in our sect, and which when properly achieved was marked by gusts of ecstatic gibberish from a prostrate and exhausted seeker.

The solemnity of these occasions was not in any way diminished by the circumstance that through the walls on Sunday evenings, from the community centre next door, which the Jewish congregation had retained when they sold the synagogue, could be heard the muted noise of laughter, and dancing, and the minor-key orientalism of a klezmer band.

Nikki was without doubt the artist of the prayer room. Ever seeking, never consoled. No one wept with more abandon. No one tarried longer. An image comes to mind, whether of one occasion or many I cannot say: Nikki's face red and swollen from prolonged weeping; sprawled, her head on one arm on the kneeling bench, the rest of her half-reclined, one leg tucked up under her skirt, the other extended on the carpeted floor; a clunky court-shoe whitened with chalky polish in the manner of those days; a still-shapeless schoolgirl calf exposed below the hem of a navy-blue dress.

We had arranged I would come back the next morning for coffee before saying goodbye. After the intensity of the night before I felt drained, and disappointed in myself. Nikki and I were the same age, but I felt I had been too old, too dull, that I had failed to rise to something that must still be there, had always been there, and was now receding for good, because I could not think what to say or do and lacked the essential courage to seize whatever it might be. I felt both relief and regret that this was over. I could not even imagine what I might have wanted, what I might have desired out of it all. Self-absorbed in this way I had not given much thought to what Nikki might have thought of the evening and of what had been said, nor thought really much about her life, as something someone had lived and was living. I realized with sadness that her life was unimaginable to me except as certain stories and recollected emotions from long ago. We were strangers to one another.

I must have been expecting Nikki to appear that morning the smart suburban matron she had first wanted me to see, and was surprised when I arrived to find that she looked as though she had not slept very well. She was serious and pensive. She stood directly in the harsh light of a window without any make-up and looked straight at me with frank appraisal and a kind of nakedness.

"Hello," I said.

"Do you want to see the rest of the house?" she said, "I haven't shown you upstairs."

"Maybe we can do that," I said.

The coffee had been made and she poured some into mugs and we sat down in her sitting room on opposite sides of an oversized coffee table of limed ash. She made no move to show me the upstairs. We sat in silence for a while.

"I have been an abused woman," she said.

We had spoken, the night before, about the breakdown of her marriage, the failures and injustices. But there was something new in her tone. The practiced ironies of the divorcée, the stagey bitterness and cynicism, were gone. She was appealing for something. Not justice. Or consolation. Maybe understanding.

"But you are free now," I said. "You survived. You have a home, successful children."

"I was a virgin when I married," she said, without preface, "I bought a nightie to wear for my husband on our wedding night and he said that it showed I had a dirty mind. He found me disgusting. After the children came he said he was impotent and that it was my fault. He found me disgusting and had rather be thought impotent than make love to me. Then I discovered he made love to other women. I lived with a cold and cruel man who oppressed me and persecuted me. I am still the prisoner of my vows. I have not had sex in twenty years. I would call that abused, wouldn't you?"

She had not shed a tear or raised her voice. She stood up.

"I don't suppose you want to see upstairs, do you?" she said.

I didn't need to answer. I finished my coffee. We said goodbye.

Lennie Gallant

Peter's Dream

I still get up before the day breaks
And I still walk down to the shore.
I watch the sun rise from the eastern ocean
But I don't sail to meet it anymore.
How could they have let this happen?
We saw it coming years ago,
The greedy ships kept getting bigger and bigger,
And the sonar told them where to go.

Last night I dreamed that I was sailing
Out on the Sea of Galilee;
We cast our nets upon the waters
And Jesus pulled them in with me.

Where am I gonna go now,
What about this boat I own,
What about this old piano,
What about my father's bones?

Last night I dreamed that I was sailing
Out on the Sea of Galilee;
We cast our nets upon the waters
And Jesus pulled them in with me.

Someone sang an old sea shanty,
And Nealy told a mainland joke.
Kelly cursed and swore until his voice gave out,
And then he asked me for a smoke,
And then he took his father's shotgun,
Walked to the harbour, through the town.
He fired fourteen times, woke everyone up,
And we all watched that boat go down.

Last night I dreamed that I was sailing
Out on the Sea of Galilee;
We cast our nets upon the waters
And Jesus pulled them in with me.

(From the albums "The Open Window" and "Live",
Revenant Records Canada.)

Wayson Choy

Proud to Be a Banana

(First printed in the Globe and Mail, July 2, 1997; revised for this publication.)

Because both my parents came from China, I look Chinese. But I cannot read or write Chinese and barely speak it: I was born in Canada. I love my North American citizenship. I don't mind being called a "banana", yellow on the outside and white inside. I'm proud to be a banana.

After all, in Canada and the United States, native Indians are "apples" (red outside, white inside); Blacks are "Oreo cookies" (black and white); and Chinese are "bananas". These metaphors assume, both rightly and wrongly, that the culture here has been primarily anglo-white. My North American birthplace and cultural history made me a banana.

History. My father and mother arrived separately to the B.C. coast in the 1900s. They came as unwanted "aliens". Better to be an alien here than to be dead of starvation in China. But after the Chinese Exclusion laws were passed in North America (late 1800s, early 1900s) no Chinese immigrants were granted citizenship in either Canada or the United States.

Like those Old China village men from Toi San who, in the 1850s, lay down cliff-edged train tracks throughout the Rockies and the Sierras, and like those first women who came as mail-order wives or concubines, and who as bond-slaves were turned into cheaper labourers or even prostitutes – like many of those North American pioneers – my father and mother survived racist, unjust times. In 1917, two hours after he got off the boat from Hong Kong, my father was called "Chink!" and told to go back to China. "Chink" is a hateful racist term, stereotyping the shape of Asian eyes: "a chink in the armour," an undesirable slit. For the Elders, the past was humiliating. Eventually, World War Two changed hostile attitudes towards the Chinese.

During the War, Chinese men and women volunteered and sacrificed their lives fighting with both the American and Canadian military. Record North American Chinatown dollars were fund-raised to buy War Bonds. After 1945, challenged by such donations and the ultimate sacrifices to Chinatown sons and daughters, the Exclusion Laws in both Canada and the U.S. were revoked. Chinatown residents claimed their citizenship and sent for their families.

By 1949, after the Communists took over China, those of us who arrived here as young children or who were born here, stayed for good in North America. No longer "aliens", we became legal citizens. Many of us also became "bananas."

Historically, "banana" is not a racist term. Though it clumsily stereotypes many of the children and grandchildren of the Old Chinatowns, the term actually follows the

191

old Chinese tendency to assign endearing nicknames to replace formal names, semi-comic names to keep one humble. Thus, "banana" describes the first generation who assimilated so well into North American life.

In fact, our families encouraged members of my generation in the 50s and 60s to "get ahead," to get an English education, to get a job with good pay and prestige. "Don't work like me," Chinatown parents said. "Work in an office!" The *lao wah-kiu*, the Chinatown old-timers, also warned, "Never forget – you still be Chinese!"

None of us ever forgot. The mirror never lied.

Many Chinatown teenagers felt we didn't quite belong in any one world. We looked Chinese, but thought and behaved North American. Impatient Chinatown parents wanted the best of both worlds for us, but they bluntly labelled their children and grandchildren *"juk-sing"* – or even *"mo no"*. Not that we were totally "shallow bamboo butt-ends" or entirely "no brain", but that we had less and less understanding of Old China traditions, and less and less interest in their village histories. Father used to say, we lacked Taoist ritual, Taoist manners. We were, he said, *"Mo li"*.

This was true. Chinatown's younger brains, like everyone else's of whatever race, were being colonized by "whitebread" family television programs. Many of us began to feel our Chinese home life and traditions were somehow embarrassing. We cooperated with English-language magazines that showed us how to act and what fashions to buy. Seductive Hollywood movies made some of us secretly weep that we did not have movie-star faces. American music made Chinese music sound like noise.

By the 70s and 80s, many of us lost our Chinatown dialects or were stuck with a child's vocabulary. We soon consciously or unconsciously distanced ourselves from our Chinatown histories. We became fluent with the lifestyles and values of the Caucasian majority, we became in-between citizens: we became bananas.

Finally, for me, in my forties and fifties, with the death first of my mother, and then my father, I realized I did not belong anywhere unless I could understand the past. I needed to find the foundation of my Chinese-ness. I needed roots.

I spent my college teaching holidays researching the past. I read Chinatown oral histories, located translated documents, searched out newspaper articles. Those early citizens came back to life for me. Their long toil and blood sacrifices, the proud record of their patient, legal challenges to racist laws, gave us all our present rights as citizens. Canadian and American Chinatowns set aside their family tong differences and encouraged each other to fight as a united community against injustice. There were no borders between Chinatowns. "After all," they affirmed, *"Daaih ga tohng yahn* .... we are all Chinese!"

In my first novel, "The Jade Peony", I tried to recreate this past, to explore the beginnings of the conflicts trapped within myself, the struggle between being Chinese and being North American. I discovered a truth: these "between world" struggles are universal.

In every human being, there is "the Other" – something that makes each of us feel how different one is to everyone else, even to family members. Yet, ironically, we are all the same, wanting the same security and happiness. I know this now.

I think that the early Chinese pioneers actually started "going bananas" from the moment they first settled upon the West Coast. They had no choice. They adapted.

They initiated assimilation. If they had not, they and their families would starve to death. I would not be here, let alone be a college English professor. I might even suggest that all surviving Chinatown citizens eventually become bananas. Only some, of course, were more ripe than others.

That's why I'm proudly a banana: I accept the paradox of being both Chinese and not Chinese. After all, I can choose from the best of both worlds. I dine at a long banquet table that includes Chinese food and hot dogs, and can take what I need and might even enjoy what others might invitingly share from their own heritage.

Now at last, whenever I look in the mirror or hear ghost voices shouting, *"You still Chinese!"*, I smile. I am a bridge between the past and the future.

I know another truth: in immigrant North America, we are all Chinese.

Liz Fleming

Finding The Boom Boom Room

T ake this card and give it to the doorman," whispered the exotically handsome concierge in the opulent lobby of the Conrad Centennial Hotel in Singapore. "You won't get in without it... and believe me... it's the best show in Singapore."

I looked at the business card I'd just been handed. Printed on cheap paper, in smudged ink, it read simply: "The Boom-Boom Room" and listed a street address. No phone number, no description of the wonders that might await us there. Just that name.

The Boom Boom Room.

It had a faintly naughty sound and that was enough for me.

I was sold.

To that point, our media tour of Singapore had been carefully arranged to show nothing that wasn't antiseptically clean or frantically well-ordered – government funded restorations and rebuilding projects, models of the city state, a pristine metro system, a glowing new arts center. In contrast to the seamy Singapore of the late 1950's and early 1960's when crime was rampant and opium houses were as common as stray cats on the street, the world we were shown was very tidy... very pleasant... and very dull. Starved for anything that wouldn't read like a tourist brochure, we thought the Boom Boom Room sounded right up our alley.

And indeed it was... up an alley... a long dark alley (very odd for Singapore, where most of the old seedy neighbourhoods were simply torn up several decades ago, and replaced with shiny new skyscrapers) that ended in an even darker doorway. Just inside, at a dimly lit table, a muscular Chinese bouncer, dressed all in black, sat cleaning his nails with a penknife. He looked at us and didn't like what he saw.

"Not your kind of place," he snarled. "You wouldn't like it. Go to Raffles. That's where all the tourists go."

Charmed by the warm welcome, I handed over the concierge's card.

The bouncer examined it carefully, looked us over again and liked what he saw on second glance even less. Half a dozen western journalists, four women and two men... white, middle-aged, middle-class and curious. We were managing to keep our notebooks in our pockets, but only just.

It was only the strength of that card that got us through the door. Without it, we'd have learned the true meaning of the term 'bouncer.'

The doorman stepped aside and in silent single file, we climbed the long, rickety staircase that led to Singapore's best kept secret.

A haze of cigarette smog hung just below the ceiling of the stairwell – this, in Singapore, where you can be fined just for thinking about smoking in a public place!

We felt the music before we heard it... a deep throbbing that shook the walls on either side of the staircase. As the last door that lay between us and the wonders of the Boom Boom Room swung open, we were dazzled by a barrage of sound, light and glitter that could have put Los Vegas to shame on its best night.

A long, raised stage dominated the room, and across it paraded some of the most stunningly gorgeous people I've ever seen. Long-limbed and full-breasted, with achingly beautiful faces and lush, long hair, wearing costumes Bob Mackie would be proud to claim, the performers danced and sang in grand-scale production numbers that electrified the room.

The face of every member of that audience turned towards the stage with undiluted adoration, their eyes following every movement. They broke into spontaneous applause and cheered as each new performer appeared. The energy pulsated as wildly as the music.

And every adoring, clapping, cheering fan gazing up at that stage was male.

And, as I'm sure you've guessed by now, every one of the achingly beautiful performers filling the stage was also male.

Every one.

All men.

All absolutely exquisite.

Through the cigarette haze and the pounding of the music, the obvious suddenly became clear. The Boom Boom Room is Singapore's best-kept secret because it is its only drag queen review. In a city state where the government scrupulously regulates and sanitizes nearly every aspect of life, the Boom Boom Room has somehow managed to avoid official notice and is flourishing...

197

improbably... but flourishing nonetheless... in the deep, dark recesses of what must surely be Singapore's last remaining back alley.

We stayed long after the rest of the city had gone to bed, laughing with the rest of the audience when the comics made jokes about the government, and clapping until our hands were sore for the incredible performers who filled the night with their singing and dancing. The rest of the audience was gracious... willing to overlook the fact that there were anatomically-correct women in the house (though certainly none of us 'regular' girls could hold a candle to any of the Boom Boom Room's women). We were allowed to melt comfortably into the crowd, though it was obvious that we might well have been the only outsiders to have done so in a very long, long time.

When at last we walked out into the sultry Singapore night, it was with the feeling that we had been allowed a glimpse into a exotic little pocket of cultural defiance... a glittering tribute to all that is not regularized, not sanitized, and not normalized, but is instead flamboyant and dramatic and exciting. We never mentioned our trip to the Boom Boom Room to our well-starched government-paid guide, nor did we ever tell anyone else where we went that night. Just where the door to the Boom Boom Room is, we can't say.

You'll have to ask the concierge for a card.

Stuart McLean

Christmas, 2007

This is the time of darkness
This is the tipping point of the year
This is when the earth tilts back on its axis
This is when the nights come early
This is when the days are short and cold
This is when it starts to get hard

All the little birds
who flew about my garden all summer
the cardinal who woke me in the early morning
and the warblers who flicked in and out of the bushes
and the thrush
but not just them
the sparrows and the crows too
those city birds
who know the luxuries of a fast food parking lot
and the heat of summer pavement
every last sodding one of them
have fled south.

Where,
I imagine,
they are perched near the edge of some warm ocean
where sea meets sand
or clustered in some mangrove
talking about chilly little me

Can you imagine, says the thrush to the warbler
He stays there all winter.
Talk about a bird brain.

The great herds of caribou have headed for their
wintering grounds

The tattered little Monarchs
Those moth like moon travellers
Have, I hope and I pray
Made it to their Mexican mountains
and God speed to them

Even the bears
who were issued fur coats at birth
have opted out
the bears, are rumbling away these dark afternoons
in mountain caves and forest hollows

This is the time of darkness
And under the cover of darkness
We gather

We gather in the synagogues
Where the bearded rabbi
Lights the second candle of Hanukkah
And places it tenderly in the menorah

And we gather in the bookstores
Where the bookseller
has already hung that neon candle
that he has hung
in the same window
every year

and we gather in the school auditoriums
where the children are singing
and in the school yards
where they are playing

And in the restaurants
and the cafés
and the coffee shops
and the bus station waiting rooms
and the hospital waiting rooms
and in the theatres
We gather

For now comes the snow
And the deep starry nights

Now comes the candles and the yule logs
And the crackling fires and all the old hymns

Now comes kitchen windows steamed and warm

Now comes hot drinks
Now comes the fellowship of breaking bread
Now comes merrymaking
and gift giving
and prayer

and my deep prayers for you
in the dark time of this year
for you and for your loved ones who are here
and your loved ones who can not be here too
who you keep thinking of in the darkness.

my prayers to you
of hope and of peace
of love and of joy

for you
and for yours
and for the nurse
who has just begun her shift

and the waitress who will soon finish hers

and for that cop
sitting alone in his car
long after the last bar has closed
and even the college kids are at home in their beds

for that cop parked there
with his coffee cup between his knees
and his radio turned low
who looks up and sees
coming right down the centre of the street
Three men leading three camels
and they don't stop at the red light

they sway right down the centre of the street
and right past his patrol car
in their solemn embroidered robes

And he is pretty sure the last in line
The one holding the gold box on the red pillow
Caught his eye as they passed
and without giving it a moment's thought
he turned off his radio
and turned on his flashing red light
and joined their solemn parade
past the dark firehall
and the empty schoolyard
and the hollow football stadium
and all the quiet stores

He followed them right to the edge of town
Where he pulled over and parked
And turned off his lights.

In the abrupt darkness
the last camel snorted
and the one carrying the gold box reached back
and steadied its snout

My prayers for him too
That cop
Who sat there
watching as the men leading the camels
disappeared
into the darkness
Their ancient eyes fixed
On God knows what star

Biographical Notes

Rona Altrows was born and raised in Montreal and now lives in Alberta. Her collection of short stories, *A Run on Hose* was shortlisted for the W.O. Mitchell Book Prize. Her work has been published in The Malahat Review, Prairie Fire and many other magazines.

Amanda Boyden grew up in Chicago and St. Louis. She teaches in the English department of the University of New Orleans. Previous positions include elderly companion, artist's model, gutter cleaner, dishwasher, science lab assistant, cancan dancer, tutor, stuntwoman, and bit part actress. Until recently, Amanda worked as a contortionist and professional trapeze artist. She is married to Canadian author Joseph Boyden. Her first novel is *Pretty Little Dirty*.

Joseph Boyden is a Canadian with Irish, Scottish, and Métis roots. His first novel, *Three Day Road* has received the Rogers Writers' Trust Fiction Prize and the McNally Robinson Aboriginal Book of the Year Award and was shortlisted for the Governor General Award for Fiction. He is the author of *Born with a Tooth*, a collection of stories. His work has appeared in publications such as Potpourri, Cimarron Review, Blue Penny Quarterly, BlackWarrior, and The Panhandler. He and his wife, Amanda Boyden, divide their time between Northern Ontario and Louisiana, where he teaches writing at the University of New Orleans.

Wayson Choy was born in British Columbia in 1939. His award-winning novels, *The Jade Peony* and *All That Matters*, and his best-selling memoir *Paper Shadows*, are all about growing up in Vancouver's Chinatown during the Depression and World War Two.

Lorna Crozier lives outside of Victoria with her husband, Patrick Lane and two fine cats. Her mother died of bowel cancer last summer.

Lorna's selected poems, *The Blue Hour of the Day*, was published in spring, 2007, by McClelland & Stewart.

Will Ferguson was born in the former fur-trading post of Fort Vermilion (pop: 840), in northern Canada, and has lived in BC, Ontario, Quebec, Ecuador, Japan, Prince Edward Island, and New Brunswick. He and his wife Terumi now live in Calgary, Alberta. His many books have included *Hitching Rides with Buddha*, *Why I Hate Canadians*, *Happiness*, and *Beauty Tips from Moose Jaw*, for which he won his second Leacock Medal for Humour.

Liz Fleming is a prolific and award-winning travel journalist, and a communications specialist, owner of Liz Fleming Communications. She lives in St. Catharines, Ontario.

David Francey was born in Ayrshire, Scotland. He is a Juno Award-winning singer. David lives with his wife, artist Beth Girdler and their three children in the quiet but charming Lanark Highlands in southern Ontario. His latest CD is *Right of Passage*.

Lennie Gallant is a singer and storyteller. A native of Rustico, Prince Edward Island, Gallant has released seven albums which have won him awards and nominations from both the Junos and the East Coast Music Awards. His newest release is *When We Get There*.

Max Gordon is a writer and activist. He has been published in the anthologies *Inside Separate Worlds: Life Stories of Young Blacks, Jews and Latinos* and *Go the Way Your Blood Beats: An Anthology of African-American Lesbian and Gay Fiction*. His work has also appeared in progressive on-line and print magazines in the U.S. and internationally, as well as in translation. He lives in New York and is currently working on a novel.

Katherine Govier is an award winning novelist with a special interest in historical figures who are artists. Her novel, *Creation*, about John James Audubon in Labrador, was a New York Times Notable Book of the Year in 2003. Her fiction and non fiction has appeared in the UK, Canada, the US, the Commonwealth and in translation in Holland, Italy, Turkey, and Slovenia. She is the winner of Canada's Marian Engel Award for a woman writer in mid-career, (1997) and the Toronto Book Award (1992). She is currently at work on her ninth novel, about Hokusai's daughter.

Anita Hanson has been an aspiring writer for the past forty-five years. Her work has been published in an anthology, in periodicals and in on-line magazines. She was recently diagnosed with ADD and is married to a saint.

David Hobson is author of two books, *Soiled Reputations* and *Diary of a Mad Gardener*. He is garden columnist for The Record in Kitchener, Ontario.

S.K. Johannesen's first novel was *Sister Patsy*, distributed by Pandora Press Publishers. Stan retired in 2004 after a 35-year career as a professor in the department of history at the University of Waterloo. He lives in Stratford, Ontario.

Stephen Kimber teaches Journalism at University of King's College. He's the author of a novel, *Reparations*, and five nonfiction books. He lives in Halifax.

Barbara Kingstone is a Member of the Society of American Travel Writers, and Co-Founder of Travel Media Association of Canada. Awards include 2003 Choice Hotels Award for Excellence in International Travel Journalism, and 2004 Starwood Hotels & Resorts Golden Click Award.

Paul Knowles' latest book is *Escaping Eden*. He has written 13 books, and writes gardening, humour, travel and feature articles for many periodicals. He also has a busy schedule as a guest speaker to gardening and community organizations.

Patrick Lane began writing with serious intent in 1960. Today, he and his wife, Lorna Crozier, reside in a small community outside Victoria where he gardens and works at his craft. His poetry, short stories, criticism, and non-fiction have won many prizes, including The Governor-General's Award for *Poems: New & Selected* in 1979, and the Canadian Authors Association Award for his *Selected Poems* in 1988. He is the author of more than twenty books and is currently working on a novel, tentatively titled *Red Dog Red Dog*.

Stuart McLean is best known for his weekly CBC Radio program, *The Vinyl Cafe*. His stories from The Vinyl Cafe have been published in four best-selling books. McLean has twice won The Stephen Leacock Medal for Humour. He often takes his show on the road, touring Canada from coast to coast.

Andrew Pyper was born in Stratford, Ontario, in 1968; he now lives in Toronto. *Lost Girls*, his first novel, was a national bestseller in Canada and a Globe and Mail Notable Book selection in 1999 as well as a Notable Book selection in the New York Times Book Review (2000) and the London Evening Standard (2000). Andrew has since written *The Trade Mission* and *The Wildfire Season*.

Paul Quarrington lives in Toronto. He is an accomplished musician and composer, a painter, and an award-winning writer, winner of the Leacock Medal for Humour. He has produced novels, sports and travel memoirs, stage plays and screenplays. His books include *Home Game*, *Whale Music*, (which won a Governor General's Award for fiction), *The Spirit Cabinet*, and *Galveston*.

Erika Ritter is a playwright, novelist, humorist, essayist, radio broadcaster, journalist, public speaker and stage performer, with plays and prose widely produced in Canada, the United States, Britain, Japan, Israel and elsewhere. She is currently at work on a new non-fiction book tentatively titled *The Dog by the Cradle, The Serpent Beneath: And Other Paradoxes of Human-Animal Relationships*, to be published by Key Porter Books in 2008.

Robin Robinson is the Travel Editor of the *Toronto Sun*, and a frequent contributor to the Sun's travel section.

Anne Stockwell is editor of *The Advocate*, and *Advocate.com*, the award-winning Lesbian, Gay, Bisexual and Transgendered magazine published in Los Angeles, California.

Jane Urquhart's books have been published in many countries, including the Netherlands, France, Germany, Britain, Scandinavia, Australia, and the United States, and have been translated into several languages. Recent novels include *The Underpainter, The Stone Carvers*, and *A Map of Glass*. Honours include the Marian Engel Award for an outstanding body of prose written by a Canadian woman, the Governor General's Award for English Fiction, France's Prix du Meilleur Livre Etranger, and the Trillium Book Award. In 1996 she was named to France's Ordre des Arts et des Lettres as a chevalier; in 2005, Urquhart was named an Officer of the Order of Canada. She is married to visual artist Tony Urquhart and divides her time between Southwestern Ontario and Ireland.